THE FALL OF CONSTANTINOPLE

THE FALL

OF

CONSTANTINOPLE

BY BERNARDINE KIELTY

Illustrated by DOUGLAS GORSLINE

RANDOM HOUSE · NEW YORK

CONTENTS

THE FALL OF CONSTANTINOPLE

1

THE FADED BRILLIANCE
OF BYZANTIUM

The Emperor stood beside a tall narrow window of his palace looking out over the housetops. It was the Blachernae Palace high on a hill in the northwest corner of the old Greek city of Constantinople. The day was March 26, 1452.

A big room stretched out behind the Emperor. It was regal in the magnificence of its proportions and the massiveness of its furniture, but the tapestries did not quite cover the stone walls. On a dais stood the throne, a gilded diadem embroidered into its high back. But the velvet cushions were threadbare. The oak beams upholding the high ceiling were blackened from fire, and the marble floor was oddly uneven. It was a palace apartment that in its day had seen strange sights and known tragic happenings.

The Emperor was Constantine XI, ruler of the empire of Constantinople and secular head of the Eastern Church of Christendom. This was not Constantine the Great, but his successor of a thousand years later. He was a Greek, by name Constantine Paleologus. His eyes were blue in his wide face, and his curling fair beard was faintly streaked with gray. He looked taller than he was because of the long narrow robe that reached to his ankles. It was royal purple as befit his rank, with a wide band of gold around his shoulders and straight down the front, which emphasized the robe's rigidity and its rich simplicity. He wore the high peaked Emperor's cap shining with jewels. But, like the room behind him, the velvet of the robe was faintly crushed and flattened, and a jewel was missing in the high pointed cap.

The Emperor had an unbroken view of his city. Down the hill below him to the east lay the narrow harbor of the Golden Horn. The sun setting behind him lighted the triangular sails of ships rounding the

Modern map showing Constantinople, now called Istanbul.

point and touched the ripples of the water with flame. Across the narrow waterway of the Golden Horn lay the hills of Galata, a town with flat-roofed houses and a single tall tower; and beyond Galata, the swift-flowing Bosporus. To the south, and west toward the setting sun, was the Sea of Marmora sprinkled with fir-clad islands. Beyond the Marmora—far beyond the view of the Emperor—stretched the great classic seas of the Western world, the Aegean and the Mediterranean.

To one who did not know, Constantinople would seem to breathe calmly in her prosperity. The great domes of the churches below looked serene and eternal in the late afternoon sun, especially Sancta Sophia, the largest of them all and the most magnificent church in the Christian world. The ships in the harbor, rocked by the breeze, spoke of good trade—of grain, spice, fruits, brought in from many lands. A caravan of camels was even now looming, heavily laden, over a hill behind Galata on the opposite shore. They were moving as fast as camels could be made to move that the drivers might pass through the city gate before it was closed for the night and get settled into one of the many caravansaries. To these traders and their drivers, after many weeks of travel through desert and mountain, Constantinople with its good food and wines and people would be a haven of joy and comfort.

But Constantine frowned as he looked down upon the familiar scene. It was a frown, not of displeasure, but of worry. For all was not serene with his beloved city. His people were in danger from an enemy that was getting closer and closer, and the Church itself was not so safe as its great spreading dome would seem to say. The Emperor was awaiting a visitor whose message would either quiet his fears, at least for a time, or threaten more than he dared let himself imagine.

He turned sadly from the outside world, bathed in sunset glow, to the darkening room behind him. Only two small lights fluttered in the shadows. They came from an alcove where a painting of the Virgin hung and shed their faint glow over her calm dignity. This was an ikon of the Greek Catholic Church, a painting on wood in dark rich colors, such as hung in every household from the poorest to the noblest, and before which the people of the household prayed. The Virgin stared straight ahead into eternity and held her child in the curve of her arm, more as a symbol than as a baby.

The Emperor went over to the saintly presence and knelt reverently before the ikon.

Lost in prayer Constantine became aware only gradually of a subdued knocking on the door. Hastily he rose and ascended the dais to his throne. Not until he had seated himself in the manner of a monarch, head high, each arm resting on an arm of the heavy chair, did he give the word for entrance.

A guard in red stepped in and closed the door behind him. It was the Emperor's own guard, Nicholas. Though his voice was precise and formal, the glance toward his master was understanding. "The Grand Chamberlain awaits your pleasure, Sire!"

At the announcement, obviously unexpected, the Emperor's face lighted up, and he stepped quickly down from the dais. "Let him in, Nicholas," he said.

Close upon the heels of the guard came an elderly man with a wise kind face. It was Phranza, Great Chamberlain and Foreign Emissary of the government.

Phranza and the Emperor greeted each other affectionately. "It was not you I awaited on my throne!" The Emperor laughed, his tenseness gone, his whole personality relaxed. They met, not as sovereign and faithful servant, but as two old friends.

Phranza had only recently returned from a two-year journey abroad. He had been delegated, as Foreign Emissary and good friend, to choose among the princesses of Eastern Europe a proper empress for Constantine. All the wealth that the country could afford —and more—had been given him for his expedition. In a fleet of many vessels he bore gifts to foreign princes; a band of musicians played for their pleasure; the riches of the greatest city in the world were flashed before the eyes of Balkan, Russian and Georgian noblemen. With him sailed physicians and monks and other men of peace.

For two years Phranza sailed the Marmora, the Aegean and the Adriatic, stopping at many ports. Last he had gone up the Bosporus to the inland Black Sea. It was here that the fortunate princess had been picked. She was a Georgian with dark slumberous eyes. She belonged to an obscure court, but she was a member of the Greek Church, prayed before the same ikons as the Emperor; and her father, in addition to a large dowry, was offering the Emperor many hardy warriors. The contract had been signed, and in a matter of a few months the future empress would be brought in state down the Bosporus to Constantinople.

"How I missed you, my noble Phranza!" Though he had seen his emissary several times since his return, each meeting was an occasion for joy.

"Even though apart we work for the same cause, Sire!"

"May we keep our promises!" said the Emperor looking into his friend's eyes. "May the fair lady finally sail into this glorious harbor!"

Phranza's nod was sympathetic.

Constantine was no longer an imposing monarch. He was a man beset with worry. History has questioned the wisdom of some of his decisions. But of all the people in that great city, now throbbing with vitality, none had its safety so close to his heart. The Emperor was a brave man and a loyal friend.

Only with Phranza could he speak openly. "You are the only one," he said gravely. "I am surrounded by suspicion and distrust. The courtiers have become restless—undependable. One in particular." Phranza nodded comprehending. "In my presence he agrees with all I say. In private he says the opposite. I cannot fight him squarely. I cannot even argue. Because he denies that we have a difference!"

Phranza knew that he spoke of the Grand Duke Lucas Notaros, admiral of the fleet, a man of enormous wealth, and second only to the Emperor in position.

"Even the monks have turned against me! They say that I am not faithful to the church! I!" The Emperor sighed.

The two men were silent, their thoughts concentrated on the darkening future.

Finally Constantine changed the subject. To cheer up his old friend he told Phranza about the next trip he had planned for him. First he should bring back the princess, then travel farther abroad. He must visit the Western powers to make friends with all.

Phranza laughed. "Your commands are irresistible, Sire," he said. "But if I am gone another two years, my wife will either get another husband or throw herself into a nunnery!"

The Emperor assured him that this would be his last service abroad. "On your return the highest position in the state will await you. And as for your son," he added, "though the boy is only fourteen, I have already found him a wealthy and noble heiress for a wife!"

Phranza bowed his head in acknowledgment, but he was silent. He could not say all that he feared. But in his own mind he determined that the trip abroad should be made not by himself but by his son; and once outside the empire, his son, with or without the wealthy noble heiress-wife, should remain there—outside and in safety. He himself would stand beside his Emperor in the troublous times that they both knew lay ahead.

When at last the Great Chamberlain left his master and friend, night had fallen and lights twinkled down below on the distant water.

Once more the Emperor girded himself for his long-expected visitor.

2

A TURK GIVES WARNING

"The Grand Vizier Khalil Pasha!" announced Nicholas the guard, when the visitor finally arrived.

Khalil Pasha, as Nicholas knew only too well, was the emissary of the Turkish Sultan Mohammed II. He was the prime minister of the powerful Mohammedan nation that was moving slowly toward them—a menacing cloud already darkening the city.

Nicholas looked at his master with concern.

Constantine nodded. Emperor and guard rarely communicated in any terms of intimacy, but between them there was confidence and understanding. The Emperor's voice when he answered was imperious and unwavering and echoed through the big half-furnished room.

"Let the Grand Vizier enter!"

He had just time enough to cross himself before the Virgin and remount the dais when Nicholas returned, this time followed by two servants bearing torches. Behind them, clad in wide brocaded coat and large white turban, strode the Emperor's visitor.

"My Lord!" He bowed his head below the Emperor's outstretched hand. But even as he paid his respects, his quick black eye darted toward the heavy hanging on the opposite wall.

"We are alone," the Emperor assured him, and the stranger could not do otherwise than believe him.

The Grand Vizier was a familiar figure to Constantine—a man past his middle years, dark-skinned and mustachioed, with long thin nose, and slender hands and feet. His clothing was rich—richer than the purple of the Emperor. By his side hung a curved sword sheathed in a highly embossed silver case—a scimitar. In his ears were large loops of twisted gold. The pointed toes of his soft narrow shoes curved upward.

These two had known each other for over a year.

They had a certain mutual respect, and as much trust in each other as men from two different civilizations can have, and from two opposing ways of worshiping God.

The Emperor knew that for whatever he learned, he must pay. He must always pay—or always promise to pay—out of the dwindling resources of his poor sick country. But he trusted this little dark man more than most. He had often before shown himself a friend of Christians and had always rendered full service for pay received. Most important for the Emperor, Khalil Pasha continued to hold his position as prime minister in the Sultan's court.

The tired blue eyes of the Christian Emperor looked into the shining black eyes of the Grand Vizier of the Ottoman Turks. "What is it you have to tell me, Khalil Pasha?"

"Peace is on his lips, but war is in his heart!" answered the Grand Vizier. No name passed his lips, but Constantine knew that he spoke of the Sultan Mohammed. "This is a conqueror. He is young. No laws bind him. No obstacle delays him. Any promise that impedes his way will be broken. If you can escape his hands, give praise to your God!"

"You ask me to leave Constantinople!" cried the Emperor, indignation underlining his words.

"He moves swiftly," the Khalil Pasha went on in a low voice. "He is ready to start building. Thirty galleys are on their way down the Bosporus carrying work-men. He himself at the head of a large army will come from Adrianople to meet them there." He nodded in the direction of the Bosporus. "The fort—the Hissar—on the Left Bank will soon be balanced by a Hissar on the Right Bank. Six miles from where we stand, two fortresses instead of one will guard that point where the banks are most close. A thousand master-builders are on their way, and for each master-builder four masons and countless common workmen!"

The Emperor shrugged his shoulders.

"My master plans to starve you!"

"The people of Constantinople will never starve!" The Emperor's voice was shrill. "Our storehouses can feed hundreds of thousands!"

"Not a mariner will dare sail his ship through this narrow passage. How will you get your grain from the steppes of Russia? How will you get the sheep of the Caucasus for your meat? How many mouths have you to feed in Constantinople?"

"About two hundred thousand!" answered the Emperor proudly.

"And for how many days and weeks and months can your supplies continue to feed your two hundred thousand hungry stomachs?"

"Until we have banished your master!" The Emperor's voice gained strength. "Until we have sent him back to the plains of Anatolia with his hordes and horses—nay, until we have sent him back to the wilds of Asia from which his ancestors sprang!"

Khalil Pasha's face tightened, but not in anger. He recognized the bravery in this Christian's words, but he also knew the savage impatience and the ferocity of that other, his master. The Vizier was not a coward himself. "Six months ago I warned you of what would happen, and that of which I warned you then has now come about. I can do no more, my friend," he said gravely. "Indeed my own position is that of a pebble in a stream. I am known already as 'friend of the Christians!' Who knows? Maybe it is on this that my life hangs: to my master I may be more valuable alive with my knowledge of you," his arm swept the city, "than dead; for with me the knowledge would die. I only tell you to prepare, if—foolhardy leader—you are unwilling to depart. Six months more and the thunder will roar and the lightning strike!"

When his visitor had gone, the Emperor once more looked out the narrow slit of window. Lights from many windows made a pattern of earthly stars. A voice from below rose in song. Was it some carefree sailor's outpouring as his ship came back to home port, oars chanting in rhythm? Or was it the raucous song from one of the too many wine cellars?

3

A STEP BACK
INTO THE DISTANT PAST

*Over a thousand years had passed from the days
of Constantine the Great to our Emperor, Constantine Paleologus, Constantine XI, standing in
his bleak Blachernae Palace.*

All that was now left of a great empire was contained
within those walls upon which the Emperor Constantine Paleologus gazed from his palace on the hill. The

Empire, of which Constantinople was the capital, had once extended from the toe of Italy to the broad Euphrates River in Asia, from the Danube in Central Europe to the falls of the Nile deep in Africa. Now it was reduced to a triangle of narrow streets, great domed churches, palaces, shops, and—in spite of what the Emperor told the Khalil Pasha—only about 100,000 people.

The Empire was now reduced to a city, but that city had endured for 1100 years, and it still stood grand and proud within its strong walls.

Constantinople is one of the four great cities of the world. For the influence it has had on our thought and our way of life it ranks with Athens, Rome and Jerusalem. Had it not been for Constantinople, we would now have no Roman law, very little Greek art, possibly not even Christianity itself. All these were preserved through eleven centuries in that stronghold of the East —the treasure house of a magnificent empire.

Many circumstances contributed to make Constantinople a city of such vast importance—the lay of the land, the climate, and its location at the meeting of three waterways.

Constantinople is a triangle bounded on two sides by water. On the northwest stretches the long curved harbor of the famous Golden Horn; to the southwest lies the Sea of Marmora; and between the two, the

18

Sea of Bosporus flows swift and strong, like a river, down from the north.

But Constantinople's waterways are not her only strength. Built on seven hills like Rome, she is also protected on the land side by these natural fortifications.

Her climate is neither too hot nor too cold. In the summer the city is cooled by strong winds from the steppes of the north, and in winter it is occasionally warmed by winds from the hot desert of the south. It is a variable climate, far brisker than the mellow lands around the Mediterranean Sea, and not unlike New York—a climate that makes its people energetic and busy and productive.

This then is the physical Constantinople.

Her history begins in 330 A.D., when Constantine the Great, Emperor of Rome, in splendor and magnificence, made Constantinople the eastern capital of the Roman world.

Or does it?

Long before the days of Constantine the Great, a small city called Byzantium lay in this same triangle. How it was founded and by whom is lost in the mists of prehistoric times. But there it was, when history dawned, a secure little city situated in the very tip of the triangle. It was Greek, it was pagan, and because of its waterways it was a busy commercial seaport.

But in those ancient days the world knew little peace.

19

Through the centuries Byzantium was caught up in the prevailing wars. She was conquered by Persia and reconquered by Greece.

The first figure to stand out boldly in those faraway times is Philip of Macedonia—a young ruler of a vigorous young country, who looked on busy Byzantium with an envious eye.

Warfare was simple in those early days. Philip's strategy for conquering Byzantium was to take it by surprise. He waited for a dark stormy night. And then, when the people were in bed, with the rain splashing and the wind howling, he sent his men into the city. They climbed the walls and made their way through subterranean passages. Silently they crept into the quiet sleeping streets.

Then, suddenly, the wind shifted. It blew away the storm clouds and uncovered the moon. So bright and so unexpected was the moonlight that the dogs began to bark, one dog after another, all over the city. The inhabitants, roused from their sleep, discovered the enemy and were immediately up in arms. Before the night was over every Macedonian in the city was slaughtered, and all the others fled.

To the Byzantines this victory over Philip was a miracle of the gods. Forever after they commemorated the event with a crescent moon. The crescent was engraved on their coins and embroidered on their banners. Crescent and star became the symbol of the city, and there it is to this day—on the flag of the final conquerors of Constantinople.

When Rome ruled the world, Byzantium became Rome's ally. It was an ideal arrangement. She remained a free city; but by her alliance with the greatest power on earth, she had that much added security.

Roman politics were complicated, however, and at her great distance from the center of things, Byzantium made mistakes. She made more than one mistake. But her final one was very serious. It was an end and a beginning.

In the fourth century A.D., two Roman emperors were pitted against each other. The quarrel in which the Byzantines became involved was between these two— the Emperor Licinius in the east and the Emperor Constantine in the west. Licinius was an old-time tyrant; Constantine, an ambitious young general—young in years but experienced in battle.

The Byzantines threw in their lot with Licinius, the older and less aggressive fighter.

These two could well have divided the Roman world between them and lived in peace. In fact they had done so for nine years.

Constantine was an adventurer. Born in wild country near the Danube, crowned Caesar in still wilder Britain, victor in a savage war fought down through the barbarian continent of Europe, conqueror of Rome—he was now almost ready to settle down. But not in Rome. For his taste Rome was a decadent, over-civilized city.

When he saw Byzantium, he knew he had found his Utopia.

"No city made by the art of man," he declared, "is so beautiful; and no site so fortified by nature!"

Nothing he had seen in all his campaigns was the equal of Byzantium.

The capture of the city was not easy. It took a violent siege, which only confirmed Constantine's admiration of its defenses.

Eventually he fought his way in. The Emperor Licinius capitulated and a year later was executed.

To make victory doubly certain, Licinius's son was also put to death.

4

THE FOUNDER —
CONSTANTINE THE GREAT

Constantine was now sole ruler of the Roman Empire. He captured the city of Byzantium in 324 A.D., and he dedicated it as his capital in 330. It was his dream to make this the greatest city in the world, and the dream came true.

First, he extended the boundaries of the city to take in the entire triangle, instead of just the tip and made plans to cover the hills with noble buildings. The riches of empire were transported to the East. Treasure came from all over the world—white marble from the island quarries, statues from the workshops of ancient Greece, delicate columns from temples, elegant friezes. Triumphal arches were erected. Walls, city gates, aqueducts were built and strengthened at enormous expense. With the treasury of Rome at his disposal and vast armies of serfs to do the work, Constantine started on such a building program as has never been equaled for speed and extravagance.

People of wealth the world over, learning of these vast plans, left Rome and the other old cities, and moved with their dependents and shiploads of household goods to this ultra-modern city. Over 400 palaces were soon built, and as many as 150 public baths. The population increased tenfold and soon outnumbered Rome.

The center of the city had always been the Hippodrome. It was an area for games, a race track for charioteers, parade ground for returning heroes, the meeting place later for tumultuous gatherings of the people, the execution ground, the backdrop of glory and tragedy. Now under Constantine's lavish hand it was enormously extended in size and enriched with ornament.

Try to imagine a vast flat oblong in the middle of the city covering nearly twelve and a half acres. In its cen-

Even Greek statues were brought to decorate the city.

ter was an Egyptian obelisk (still standing) and at one end, the throne of the emperor. Down its great length stood rows upon rows of gigantic outlandish figures—a Giant Maiden who held in her right hand a horse and rider, *life-size;* a Hercules of bronze so huge that an ordinary man reached only to his kneecap; an enormous Enraged Elephant; Helen (of Paris and Menelaus fame); eight Sphinxes; a She-Wolf and Hyena, from which in later days the angry mob hanged a traitor emperor, head down.

This was not Great Art. It was Big Art. But it stunned the world of its day. As time went on, the statues increased in number until they almost outnumbered the living—a grotesque unhuman world of brass and bronze and marble.

(The Hippodrome adornment best known to the modern world was a group of four prancing gilded horses. These same ancient horses can now be seen in Venice guarding the main entrance to St. Mark's Cathedral—stolen from Constantinople, as we shall see, by Venetian marauders in the thirteenth century.)

On the day of the dedication of the city—May 11, 330—a long procession marched through the newly paved roadways and into the Hippodrome. From his throne at the north end, the Emperor viewed the thousands of sturdy citizens now staring open-eyed with wonder. Grouped around him were his relatives. Not his wife, Fausta, because he had had her smothered in

26

her bath; not his oldest son, Crispus, who had been secretly condemned to death; not his mother, St. Helena,
because she had already died a natural death. All
the other princes were present, however, alive, alert,
eager—little knowing that wars would soon make
enemies of them all and hurl them bitterly against one
another. Senators from Rome encircled the family, con-
suls, patricians and magistrates, all in robes of splendor. On the benches along the sides sat citizens of rank;
and standing in packed crowds the length of the Hippodrome were the masses of the miscellaneous poor
that made up the noisy rabble of the city.

The dedication festivities lasted forty days.

Constantine the Great was the first Christian Roman
Emperor. The story goes that Constantine once had a
vision. At noonday, in the sky, he saw a fiery cross with
words of flame: "By this sign, conquer." This was
the sign, says an old tale, by which he was converted to
Christianity.

How good a Christian he was and how true the
story, it is not for us, in our day, to judge. In the beginning of the fourth century, the Christians made up only
a small proportion of the inhabitants of the Roman
Empire. But they were a firmly united little group that
could be of great help to any popular leader to whom
they devoted themselves. The father of Constantine,
Constantius, always held the Christians in high es-
teem, and rewarded them in many ways; and Constan-

tine himself, even before he became converted to Christianity, made himself their protector. He was tolerant; he encouraged Christian leaders to preach their faith; he stood behind them. When a city of the Empire destroyed its pagan temples, he gave that city a reward.

Possibly Constantine the Great saw Christianity as the religion of the future. Whether he became converted because of policy, or a vision, or even remorse for some of his own evil deeds, no one knows. But the fact remains that his reign was the turning point in the history of Christianity. Many of the nobles followed his example and became Christians in order to be in the Emperor's good graces if for no other reason. As each person of rank was converted, hundreds of others belonging to his household did the same. In Rome 12,000 men were said to have been converted in a year, and Constantinople boasted that the city had never been profaned by the worship of idols.

Soldiers and traders and peddlers carried the knowledge of the Gospel to lands outside the Empire, and it took the barbarians very little time to be converted. Here was a religion, as they saw it, introduced by the most powerful monarch of the most advanced nation in the world. It behooved them to join its ranks.

Over a thousand years had passed from the days of Constantine the Great to our Emperor, Constantine

Paleologus, Constantine XI, standing in his bleak Blachernae Palace. None of the same blood flowed in the veins of these two, who lived one at the beginning and the other at the end of that long passage of history. They shared a name and a religion only. In the centuries that lay between these two, the city progressed from the first Christian city, to the strongest Christian city, in the world.

5

THE CITY BECOMES AN EMPIRE—
JUSTINIAN AND THEODORA

For 1100 years Constantinople remained the capital
of the Roman Empire of the East—the bulwark
against all non-Christian peoples. During those centuries there were eleven dynasties, eleven large families
who ruled the empire, some wisely, some badly. But
the weakness and the sinfulness of their rulers failed
to undermine the integrity and honor of the people.

Dynasties came and went. But the citizens remained steadfast.

Let us take some well-spaced steps down through history. Let us get a close look at a few faces that shine through the mists of time and see the dramatic episodes in which they figured.

Probably the most illustrious name in the entire history of Constantinople is that of Justinian the Great, emperor from 527 to 565 A.D.

Even today our lives are affected by the "Justinian Code." Justinian had been educated in law and administration, and his first great project was to revise and simplify Roman law which by this time had become hopelessly confused. What he did was to discard the obsolete and useless and clarify what remained. It was a stupendous undertaking, *not* appreciated by the people of his day, but enough to make him, for future generations, one of the greatest of emperors.

Justinian also built the magnificent church of Sancta Sophia whose glorious dome still dominates the city. It is an enormous dome, 180 feet above the ground, but so delicately poised that it seems to float. In Justinian's day it was lined with glittering mosaics that told the whole story of Christianity in gold and jewel-like colors. White columns of marble upheld the many arches of the aisles. The altars were ablaze with gold and silver. "O Solomon!" Justinian cried out when the noble church was finished. "I have surpassed thee!"

This monument of art his contemporaries *did* appreciate. Travelers came from distant lands to see it, and the people of the city crowded into it to adore.

Under Justinian the language of the Empire became completely Greek. Latin was forgotten. The city, its art, its architecture, its customs, became very distinctive—different both from the West and from the oriental. As a style of art, even as a way of life and dress, it gradually came to be known as "Byzantine," partly to distinguish it from ancient Greek, partly because of its own special qualities.

Justinian was almost as famous for his wife as for his deeds. *The Justinian Code, the church of Sancta Sophia,* and *Theodora!*

The Empress Theodora with whom he shared his throne came from the poorest of the poor in Constantinople. She was a comedienne in a carnival show where her father was master of the bears. She puffed up her cheeks and rolled her eyes and made the audience laugh and applaud. More important for her future, she was incredibly beautiful. Pictures and mosaics of her remain; and we can see the delicacy of her features, the vivacity of her eyes, the suggested grace of her movements.

She was also clever. When the young noble Justinian saw her, he at once fell in love. And once in love he could never escape. Not that he wanted to. Theodora became his strong and powerful co-ruler for twenty years, and he is said to have remained forever faithful and in love.

Great calamities, as well as great benefits, befell the earth during Justinian's reign.

An earthquake shook Constantinople for forty days, its shock spreading over the whole surface of the land. Approximately 250,000 persons are said to have been killed.

Comets were seen in the skies, which terrified the people who in those days knew little of astronomy.

One of the great plagues of all time broke forth in the fifteenth year of Justinian's reign. It moved from hot to temperate countries, from the seacoast inland, spreading from country to country by the intermingling of people in war and emigration. In those days when there was no inoculation or vaccination, a disease had to wear itself out. It took this one fifty-two years to do so. Whole cities were wiped out. Thousands of persons died daily in Constantinople, and many of the poor lay unburied in the streets.

Yet the city grew.

Caravans bearing goods came from the east, ships from the west. With the glory of her churches and the palaces of her emperors, Constantinople became the great capital of the world. The literature of ancient Greece remained alive in her libraries. In that triangle of hills, dampened by salt spray and wind, a race of hardy men and women went on living, and civilization survived.

The emperors were despots. Even the best of them were cruel. But the people remained patient, strong and enduring. As Constantine the Great had foreseen, the city, in its strategic position, was able to hold off the enemy on all sides. It withstood onslaught after onslaught—of Tartars, Bulgars, Huns, Goths, Slavs. It held out. More than that, it became a fighting, aggressive, victorious nation.

While Constantinople was thus waxing rich and powerful, western Europe was disintegrating into a wilderness. Barbarians overran the continent and Italy. Rome became no more than a country town. Actually for one short period not a living soul was left in Rome except the wolves and rats. A barbarian conqueror, fearing insurrection among the conquered Romans, removed the entire population.

The Dark Ages had descended. A curtain of confusion and ignorance was drawn over what was once the mighty Roman Empire. Only in Constantinople, of all the civilized world, was the light of learning kept brightly burning. In the churches of that strong city the faith of Christianity glowed like a beacon in a dark world.

6

THE PROPHET MAHOMET

The Dark Ages drew a curtain down over Europe. For hundreds of years civilization withered. Outside of monastery cells there was no art, no literature, no safety. No roads were protected; there was little trade and only a few scattered schools. For four centuries the minds of people were sunk in ignorance. Grass grew in the streets of mighty Rome.

That was Christian Europe.

But during those same years a dynamic force was gathering strength in the East. Like a hurricane it began its gyrations in one small area, then whirled forth to shatter the world with its might. It was nurtured, not by a political creed or a conqueror's ambition, but by a religion. Like Christianity, that religion reverenced one God. His name was Allah. It had one prophet, and he was Mahomet. And as a powerful force in history, this religion plays an all-important part in the story of Constantinople.

It is a curious and provocative fact that Christianity and Judaism and Mohammedanism—three of the world's greatest religions—all came into existence in the same small corner of the world. This is the area between the south shore of the Mediterranean Sea and the Red Sea, the hills of Judea, the mountains of Arabia and the desert. It is warm there. The climate is sultry. There are date trees, flocks, camels, tents. Life is not so strenuous as in the cold climes of Europe. A man in those early days had leisure to think as he watched his sheep, or jogged along on his camel, or gazed up at the stars from the entrance of his tent. It was a life of loneliness and there grew up in that region men of imagination—visionaries—mystics. They found the heavens, and they showed us the way.

Mohammedanism grew into being in the desert of Arabia.

The people of Arabia—the Arabs—were brothers of the Hebrews. They were Semites. Like the Hebrews of the Bible, they called Abraham their father. Through his wife Sarah, he "begat" the Hebrews. By a slave, Hagar, he "begat" the Ishmaelites, who are the Arabs. Hagar's child, Ishmael, wandering with his mother through the hot desert, cried out with thirst. Bitterly he dug his heel into the sand, and thereupon a spring of water gushed forth. This is the story of the oasis on the desert which became the town of Mecca. The spring became Mecca's famous wells, where Abraham and Ishmael built a temple; and Mecca became a place of pilgrimage.

This was back in earliest Bible times.

In the days of the Roman Empire, in the days of Constantine the Great and of Justinian, and of the emperors of Constantinople who immediately followed them, the land of Arabia was practically unknown. It was a wide, dry, limitless desert lying somewhere between Egypt and the Red Sea. Over it wild tribesmen in flowing white robes rode galloping steeds. Over its desert sands caravans of camels moved slowly back and forth like ships on the ocean. There were no farms. There was no cultivation of the land—only sand, desert, horsemen. A small amount of trading was carried on, but it made no impression on the minds of emperors, kings and conquerors. For them Arabia scarcely existed.

Mahomet, the Prophet, from whom this new religion sprang like a great tree from a tiny seed, was born about 570 in Mecca. He was born into a family of no distinction. But Mecca, of all Arabia, was the one town which had some dealings with the rest of the world. It was a town of pagan temples. It was a trading post. And when Mahomet was still a lad, he got work with a camel caravan that carried goods to places far away.

On one of these journeys across the desert, when he was only thirteen, Mahomet met a Christian monk named Djerdjis (George). The two became great friends—the old monk and the earnest young boy. It was a friendship which must have made a profound impression on Mahomet.

Not many years later Mahomet married the woman who owned the caravan business for which he worked, a wealthy widow, older than himself. This gave him a certain standing in Mecca, and it also sent him on more journeys, to more distant places where he met other Christians and Jews.

Mahomet was an ignorant, uneducated man, but he was reflective. Each time that he returned to the desert he thought about what he had seen and heard, and out under the starry sky where he was much alone, he pondered on the weakness of man and the strength and glory of God—Abraham's God—the *only* God, as he now felt Him to be.

Mahomet was a reformer. He wanted to help his fellow men become better and stronger. But it was not until he was well along toward middle age, around the age of forty, that he became a mystic and began to preach to them in terms of religion. Once in the desert, alone, surrounded by sand and sky, he had a vision, and after this, many visions. Each time he would fall into a trance and see the spacious landscape of paradise, and the torments of Hell, and the terrible day of Judgment.

At first Mahomet told only his wife and his closest friends about these visions, but in time the circle of listeners widened. Small groups of disciples began to gather around him, and he spoke to them with the upsurging force of one inspired.

Unto those who believe and do good works . . . theirs will be Gardens of Eden wherein rivers flow beneath them. Therein they will be given armlets of gold and will wear green robes of finest silk and gold embroidery, reclining upon thrones therein.

And Lo! For the transgressors there will be an evil journey's end. Hell, where they will burn, an evil resting place. . . . For those who disbelieve. . . . Lo! they will roast at the fire. Garments of fire will be cut out for them; boiling fluid will be poured down on their heads. . . .

It is these fearful threats and glorious promises of reward and the sound practical advice that followed them that make up what we now know as the Koran, the Holy Book of Mohammedanism.

Mahomet was a tall spare man with a thin straight beard. His hair was black and his eyes were dark and piercing. He lived humbly. The garment he wore was of coarsest wool and his feet were often bare. He milked his own sheep, fetched his own water, swept and washed his own floor. Sitting on a straw mat, he mended his sandals.

With the poor and the ill he was gentle and soft-spoken. But when he preached, his voice rang, and his listeners stood spellbound.

As in the Christian credo, the Koran preaches brotherly love. Like the Jews and Christians, Mahomet preached one God (Allah). "Islam" means submission to Allah's will. "Moslem" means one who submits. Like Christians and Jews, Mohammedans honor the prophets of the Bible from Abraham to Christ. But of them all, Mahomet is the greatest prophet.

Above all, Mahomet denounced idols and superstition. This was his most daring pronouncement. For Mecca was the center of the Arab pagan religion, a town of pagan shrines and temples, and one to which the idolators of the desert made pilgrimages. With the exception of Mahomet and his few followers, all the inhabitants of Mecca were pagans. For a time they only laughed at this dreamer. They called him mad. Later they scorned and tormented him.

For fifteen years Mahomet endured this humiliation and increasing opposition. Then he escaped to Medina. This journey from Mecca to Medina in the year 622 was called the Hegira; and among Mohammedans, the Hegira marks the beginning of the Moslem era.

At Medina, the second largest town in Arabia, Mahomet came into his own. There he acquired many followers and began to make the laws and practice of the new religion more definite.

He forbade his people wine or any other fermented liquor: *O ye who believe! Strong drink and games of chance are only an infamy of Satan's handiwork. Leave it aside in order that ye may succeed.* . . .

He ordered them to fast: *O ye who believe! Fasting is prescribed for you.* . . . *Fast the month of Ramadan.* . . .

He demanded bodily cleanliness and daily prayer: *O ye who believe! Draw not near unto prayer till ye have bathed.* . . . *If ye find not water, then go to high clean soil and rub your faces and your hands therewith.* . . .

When he finally returned to Mecca, he came as an

accepted leader with a great body of disciples who were already putting his teachings into practice. Mecca, instead of a pagan center, now became the Mohammedan Holy City which it remains to this day. When a good Moslem kneels to pray—as he does five times a day—his prayer rug always points to Mecca. When he bows his head and salaams, it is toward Mecca.

Because his teachings were practical and because he was such an ardent orator, Mahomet succeeded in uniting the Arabian peoples within his own lifetime. The wild tribesmen were quieted by daily prayer. Enforced abstinence from liquor and gambling made their soldiers superior in strength to other armies. The shepherd nomads soon became fighting conquerors.

As the followers of Mahomet come down through history, we hear them called first Saracens; then Moors, particularly in Spain; Mohammedans and Moslems. Their religion has lasted 1300 years and numbers second among the religions of the world today. (There are nearly twice as many Mohammedans in the world now as there are Protestant Christians.)

Now, as in the day of Mahomet himself, at sunset and sunrise, the crier called the muezzin climbs to the top of a slender circular tower (the minaret), and facing in turn the four points of the compass, calls the faithful to prayer. As he chants, the men gather at the fountains to wash. They take off their shoes, because shoes are forbidden, and softly they file into the mosque, the Mohammedan place of worship. Once in his lifetime every "true believer," if it is physically possible, makes a pilgrimage to Mecca.

Mahomet died in 632 in the sixty-third year of his life; and in a hundred years, as we shall see, his followers had conquered a large part of the known world. Even within the lifetime of men who had known the prophet, Mohammedanism extended from a pinpoint in the Arabian desert to a vast area that stretched from the Indus River in Asia to the Atlantic Ocean.

In the beginning these Arab shepherds were not fighting to convert the world to Islam. They were only out to raid and plunder. First they conquered the villages nearest them and then pushed on. But each village that they conquered, they held. The Moslem religion being one of the brotherhood under God, its people recognize no differences in color, race or nation. So these Mohammedan Arabs, Saracens as they were then called, were tolerant of the Christians and the Jews that they found in the villages. In fact, they used the gifts of these conquered peoples for the good of all. They administered well. And they continued to push ahead.

They took Egypt in 642, and in 650 they took the entire Persian Empire. By now they were fighting for a religion. Church bells were silent, and the muezzin call to prayer took their place. Before the year 700 the

Saracens had overrun all of North Africa and, shortly afterward, nearly all of Spain.

Constantinople shook as the hoofbeats of the Saracens trampled the mountains and plains of Asia Minor.

7

THE SARACENS TRY TO CONQUER THE CITY

After the death of Mahomet, the Saracens fastened their gleaming eyes on Constantinople. The prophet had said that the first army to besiege that city would have its sins forgiven. "Happy the prince, happy the army, that shall achieve its conquest."

Mahomet had been dead no more than forty years when his followers made their first attempt. For six long years a Moslem army tried to wear down the resistance of the city. But the walls of Constantinople stood firm. And the enemy leader, an aged Caliph, finally gave up, broken-hearted and defeated.

For an entire generation after this debacle the Saracens stayed away, licking their wounds.

Not until 717 did they reassemble their forces for a second attempt—a siege far more formidable than the first, both in numbers and strength, and in results even more humiliating for the besiegers.

The Moslems had learned from previous experience that they could not break through the impregnable walls. So this time they planned an invasion by sea. There were said to be 1800 ships assembled and troops standing by to the number of 120,000.

That Constantinople withstood the strain of such a siege, and finally ousted such a mighty force, was due solely to the adroitness of the Emperor Leo, known as Leo the Isaurian. Leo was a great emperor and an able general—a peasant who became a soldier of fortune, who fought spectacularly and rose to the top on ability alone. He was still young.

Leo was an astute planner. Knowing that his people were in for a long siege, he had gathered provisions during the many months that the Saracens were on the march. Since there still remained the fear of starvation if the ship blockade should succeed, he did what he could to strengthen his own ships. They were far too few in number to make an offensive, but they were safely protected by a tremendous chain thrown across the entrance of the harbor, which prevented any outside ships from getting in. This is the Boom of which we shall hear much more. He also had a devastating secret weapon of which we also shall hear throughout the entire military history of Constantinople. This was the terrifying "Greek fire."

(Greek fire is believed to have been a mixture of naphtha, sulfur and pitch. But the formula was a secret, and the men who made it had their tongues cut out for "security" reasons. The secret belonged to Constantinople alone and was held for 400 years.)

So here was the Emperor Leo with a stout citizenry well provided for, with strong walls and fortifications surrounding them, with some good ships in a well-protected harbor, and the deadly "Greek fire."

The bitter cold winter of 717 killed off thousands of the besiegers, who were used to warmer climes; and the strong wind and currents in the Bosporus incapacitated their ships for action. By spring their forces were badly decimated.

This was the time that Leo chose for his big coup. All winter the heavy chain had kept the harbor closed. Now he slyly opened it up to lure the enemy. As the enemy ships approached the harbor, the imperial ships, ready and waiting, deluged them with Greek fire. The result was complete annihilation.

Greek fire poured on them from every direction—from the ships, from the walls of the city, from the mainland. In the confusion of trying to escape, ships dashed against each other. Men jumped into the sea and were drowned. Hulls were cracked, masts broken, oars lost. In the strong current of the Bosporus, many of the ships were overturned and sunk. By the time the battle was over, not a Moslem ship remained in sight. Only five ships, it is said, returned to Syria to tell the tale.

The tale they told was of Greek fire—fire that could be poured on the enemy from large boilers on a rampart or hurled in red-hot balls of stone and iron, that could be darted forth in arrows and javelins soaked in the liquid, or blown through long tubes of copper planted on the prow of a ship. Black smoke. A deafening explosion. Then a spreading flame that nothing could stop and that flowed upon the water!

Had Constantinople fallen in 717, Christianity could not have survived. To Leo the Isaurian we owe the safety of the city and of Christendom for the next 500 years. But for him the whole course of history might have been changed. Had the Moslems succeeded in 717, ours might now be a Moslem world.

8

CONSTANTINOPLE AT ITS PEAK—
THE MILLENNIUM

After this crushing defeat of the Moslems in 717 and
for the next 300 years, the Byzantine Empire flourished as never before. Constantinople became stronger,
richer, more confident. The Saracens were scattered in
far separated centers—in Bagdad, Damascus, Cor-
dova. The Byzantines, or the Greeks as we shall often
call them, were no longer on the defensive. They had

The Byzantine Empire

Venice

CORSICA

Rome

SARDINIA

ADRIATIC SEA

DALMATIA

MEDITERRA

AFRICA

SICILY

SEA OF AZOV

CAUCASUS

BLACK SEA

Constantinople

SEA OF MARMORA

• Brusa

ARMENIA

• Smyrna

RHODES

CYPRUS

SYRIA

AN SEA

Nile

WONG

e covered 650,000 square miles.

now turned conquerors. By the year 1000, the first millennium, their empire covered 650,000 square miles and numbered 2,000,000 inhabitants.

The Emperor Basil II became the first Byzantine or Greek imperialist. Under him Constantinople reached its greatest magnificence. It was a marvel of riches known in all corners of the world.

From much that still survives and from the letters and diaries of traders who visited it at that time, we know with fair exactness just how the city looked.

The Emperor's palace was incredibly grand. In its grounds overlooking the Sea of Marmora, were pavilions, gardens, baths, libraries, prisons, houses for thousands of officials and servants, terrace upon glittering terrace. The great residence buildings themselves were decorated with marbles and porphyry, paintings and sculpture. There was a fountain lined with silver which once a year was filled with exquisite fruits and opened up to the populace. From his golden throne at the top of a great stairway, the Emperor could gaze down upon his people clamoring for a pear or a pomegranate.

Sancta Sophia, the magnificent church, was the center of all religious festivals. Here the people gathered by thousands in the light of huge silver candelabra and high swinging lanterns. Above them the enormous dome floated in a sea of light; and the chanting of the choir, losing itself in the lofty roof, seemed to mingle with the voices of angels descending from heaven.

Bazaars stretched for miles. Everything made in the world of that day could be bought there—embroideries, jewels, carved ivories, enamels, perfumes, incense. In its winding alleys could be seen faces from every land—dark-skinned Arabs, wide-faced Russians, long-nosed Venetians, Italian fishermen, Jewish traders, Armenian shepherds there to sell their sheep, Hindus, Negroes, even the occasional flat face of a Chinese. Scandinavians and Anglo-Saxons came in their long ships.

Yet Constantinople was Greek to its fingertips.

There were hospitals and universities, orphan asylums, a school of law, a medical school, and monasteries and nunneries. There were also slums—filthy narrow streets, unpaved and muddy, where dogs whined throughout the night, where thieves hid, where dens of sinfulness flourished. "If Constantinople surpasses all other cities in riches," wrote one of its many visitors, "so does it also in vices."

Palatial homes, surrounded by lovely terraced gardens, lined the coasts and islands of the Marmora and both the Asiatic and European shores of the Bosporus. These were the estates of the nobles.

But Constantinople itself was the center. It was the heartbeat of the Byzantine Empire as Paris has always been the heartbeat of France.

The emperors lived like gods. Anyone who entered

the emperor's presence must prostrate himself while the monarch himself remained rigid on his throne. The emperor's garment was often so stiff with brocade and jewels that he could not sit down. His diadem was heavy with gold and silver and pearls that descended in strands to his shoulders. The golden lions on either side of his throne bellowed, and mechanical birds sang from on high.

Sometimes a startled visitor, after salaaming before the emperor, raised his head only to find the emperor high in the air before him, throne and all. This was a trick managed by concealed pulleys, and designed for just this purpose—to astound the common man.

When the emperor left the palace, heralds rode ahead warning the inhabitants to sweep the streets and to scatter perfumes and flowers before him. Borne aloft on a platform carried by slaves, his hair and beard dyed auburn, and his lips and cheeks painted vermilion, his long robe embroidered in gold and jewels, he was indeed a strange god.

But all was not show and glitter. The government of the Empire was sound. It provided the safest life of any city in the world at that time and for several centuries to come. While Paris and London were drinking water from filthy wells, the water of Constantinople, brought in by long aqueducts, was pure. Law and order were enforced. Even a man of the modern world

The emperor was borne on a platform carried by slaves.

could have lived there in comfort and safety and with plenty of intellectual stimulation.

In commerce as well as culture, Constantinople was the center of the world. Traders came to sell their wares and buy other goods. Caravans came from the east and north, ships from the south and west. India sent jewels and spices; China, silk; Bagdad and Syria brought carpets. From north of the Black Sea came wheat and furs; grain and flax from the Balkans; and from the west—kidnaped from all the lands from Norway to Italy—came slaves.

Constantinople had its own industries, all regulated and protected and heavily taxed. It owned vast cattle ranges in Anatolia (Asia Minor) and wheat fields in northern Greece.

At the death of Basil II, the treasure of the palace at Constantinople amounted to forty million dollars, an amount which would be worth many times that now. In the year 1000 the Emperor of Byzantium was the richest ruler in the world.

9

INFIDELS AND CHRISTIANS

(An infidel is one who does not accept a particular faith. In the Middle Ages it was a term used
widely to mean Mohammedans, and we shall
therefore use it that way. But it must be remembered that to a Mohammedan in those days an
infidel meant a *Christian*.)

The year 1000 saw Constantinople at the height of
her glory—a paradise of gold and silk and pearls and

marble, her emperors rich and haughty and unapproachable, trade flourishing, churches filled with devout Christians.

It saw Europe a wilderness of forests and backward people.

Far away on the plains of Central Asia it saw a new restless force gathering momentum.

North of the great mountains of India, between the Caspian Sea on the west and the land of ancient China on the east, lived bands of nomad tribes. Like all peoples in those remote times and far distant places, they were constantly on the move. They were forever pulling up stakes, folding up their black tents and riding forth to seek new grazing ranges for their sheep. It was cold on those windswept plains, and the cold stirred the blood to action.

Among these roaming tribes were the Turks.

When first their trail crossed the path of history, the Turks were nomads, shepherds, horsemen. In those early days they had no home. They had no culture. If they had a religion, it was pagan. But even then they were outstanding among all tribes as fighters. War was their delight. Their leaders learned early how to build armies and how to enforce discipline. To die in battle was said to be the ambition of every normal Turk. To die in bed seemed shameful.

On the borders of Persia, these roaming fighters came across the Saracens—the Arab Mohammedans, by now a settled people with regular armies. Desirous of getting into these armies, many of the fighter Turks adopted the Saracen religion. It spread like wildfire among their fellow tribesmen; and by the year 1000 it might be said that the Turks as a people had been converted to Mohammedanism.

This was a momentous event. For these two forces—the fighting Turks and the Mohammedan religion—made an invincible combination. Were it not for Mohammedanism, the Turks would doubtless still be herding sheep in Central Asia; and were it not for the Turks, Mohammedanism might have withered and died.

With scimitar in one hand and Koran in the other, the Turks established Mohammedanism as a lasting, widespread religion. To make converts at the point of the sword was the Turks' natural bent in those days, and in this spirit they set out to conquer the world.

The first Turks to get a foothold in Asia Minor were the Seljuks. Under their Sultan, Alp Arslan, they came out of the east and descended upon Armenia, the richest farm land of the region, only lately annexed to the Byzantine Empire.

This was a challenge to Constantinople—to the fathers of the city who for so long had been secure in their gilded complacency, and to Emperor Romanos IV who set out eastward in 1071 with the Byzantine army to push back the threatening force. Weighed down with heavy armor, the Greeks had a hard time pursuing the swift, lightly clad Turkish horsemen. But once they met face to face, the Greeks had the advantage. They met on the borders of Armenia; and the Battle of Manzikert, which marked their meeting, has come down as one of the decisive battles of history.

Safe in their heavy armor, the Greeks were fighting valiantly against the Turkish archers and holding their own. Indeed the battle might well have been a victory for Byzantium had it not been for the treason of a Greek. The traitor was one Andronikos. Instead of bringing his men up to help the hard-fighting front line as ordered, he led them back to camp; and the soldiers of the front line had to fight on unaided. This they did until the last man dropped. When the battle was finally ended, the Emperor Romanos was dragged out from under his dead horse and carried in triumph to the tent of the Turkish Sultan. There, as a mark of victory, Alp Arslan put his foot on the neck of his vanquished foe.

This was the beginning of the end.

City after city of the rich Byzantine Empire now fell to the seemingly invincible Seljuk Turks. For the next ten years they burned their way across Asia Minor. The farm lands that had been feeding the empire for hundreds of years were reduced to grazing ground. The peasants who had been the backbone of the imperial army became captives. The next ten years the

Seljuks went farther. And the next ten, farther still. Altogether they fanned out over the Byzantine Empire for a period of more than a hundred years.

But they were never quite strong enough to attack its core—the still powerful, impregnably walled Constantinople.

Through this stretch of a hundred years, many a weak emperor ruled over Constantinople, jeopardized its power, undermined its resources. Then a single emperor would rise who was strong enough to stand firm and to recover some of what had been lost, of prestige even if not of territory.

Such an emperor was Alexios Komnenos, whom we are about to meet. Such—400 years later—was Emperor Constantine Paleologos.

10

THE CRUSADES

It was in defiance of the Turks that the Western world now turned its heavy gaze eastward. Europe—abode of rough barons and fighting dukes, continent of forests, isolated castles and few cities—was now slowly awaking from its long sleep of the Dark Ages. The nobles of regions that are now France, England, Spain and Germany were beginning to feel their power. Knighthood was beginning to hold its own. The trading cities of Venice, Pisa and Genoa were emerging as republics. The Church of Rome was coming out of its obscurity.

Religion, which had remained alive for four centuries principally in monasteries and convents, now took on new life in the world outside the cloister. The great cathedrals of Europe were started at this time, built by the hands and artistry and love of the people themselves. A genuine religious revival had begun.

The Crusades, which lasted over a period of roughly two hundred years, were one of the chief outlets of Europe's new-found energy. They waved the banner of Christianity and for the moment held its torch high.

With the exception of the disastrous Fourth Crusade, the Crusades were not of all-out importance to our story. They brushed against the golden giant, Constantinople, it is true, and they constituted a spectacular episode in history. But their greatest significance for our purposes was the growing bitterness which they nurtured between the East and the West.

The Crusades started in the eleventh century, after the conversion of the Turks to Mohammedanism, after the Seljuks had captured most of the cities of Asia Minor, after the fateful Battle of Manzikert.

Constantinople at this time was still phenomenally rich and powerful. But the enemy was getting uncomfortably close. Now only a strip of water separated her from the victorious Turks.

Alexios Komnenos was the emperor, a man both able and sly. He was in a tight spot and he needed help.

One day, as if in answer to his prayer, a simple creature wandered into the Emperor's court. It was Peter the Hermit. Peter had come from Europe on a pilgrimage to the Holy Land as had many others of the devout. He had visited Jerusalem and was deeply shocked to see Christians living there under the rule of infidels. He then made his way to the great city of Constantinople and, in his simple ignorance, into the very presence of the mighty Emperor. He had come to report what he had seen.

Emperor Alexios, sensing the power of the fanatic in this simpleton, further kindled the flame by adding a terrifying picture of his own of the infidel's cruelties and blasphemies.

Peter was appalled. "I will rouse the warriors of Europe to your cause, Sire," he cried. And Alexios solemnly raised his hand in princely blessing.

Peter returned to Europe. This meant a journey of many months, for time and travel moved slowly in those days.

Once back in Europe Peter got a small donkey and, carrying a heavy crucifix, he rode through the villages of France and Italy, stirring the people to action. In the churches, on the highways and in the market places, he gathered them to him and told of the sufferings and the indignities of Christians in the Holy Land. His head was uncovered; his feet were bare; his thin emaciated body was wrapped in a rough garment. He ate little; he prayed long; and the money people gave him he gave back to those who needed it.

His listeners sobbed with emotion.

Alexios could not have had a better advocate. Nor could the Pope be better satisfied. For, as the Greeks wanted help from the West to oust the Turks from their borders, so the West wanted much from the East. Above all things, the Pope wanted to see the Greek Orthodox church and the Roman church united. Therefore, to all who would go to the Holy Land to fight the infidel, the Pope offered an indulgence, that is, penance for past sins.

So began the First Crusade. Leading the procession, rode Peter the Hermit on his donkey in company with two others. On one side was a goat, on the other a waddling goose. These symbolized the Holy Ghost. Straggling behind Peter were the sinners of the Western world—the outlaws, thieves, robbers, assassins, murderers—all who wanted to have their sins forgiven and have an adventurous journey at the same time. Among them were also many sincere, devout, holy men.

Painfully, this miserable mass made its way across Europe toward the East—60,000 men and women, many of them dying by the wayside. When they finally

reached Constantinople—dirty, diseased and dying—
they numbered only 40,000. At least 20,000 had died
or returned.

The Emperor Alexios looked at this rabble aghast.
His one thought was to get them out of the city as fast
as possible. In no time at all he had them rowed across
the Bosporus to Asia where the infidel held sway, and
no sooner had the raggle-taggle crowd landed in Asia
than they were attacked by the vigorous troops of the
reigning Turkish Sultan and promptly massacred.
Nothing was left, it is said, except a pile of bones.

Peter himself remained in Constantinople and lived
out the remainder of his life there, regarded by all as
a harmless lunatic.

But this was only a brief prelude to the real Crusades. The movement had started. Nearly every year
now saw a new band of fighting pilgrims coming to the
Holy Land. Some were holy men, more were adventurers. The flow of new forces eastward and back, begun so casually—so almost ridiculously—continued for
many generations.

On the heels of Peter's rabble, in 1097, came the
great war lords of Europe with their retinues. Theirs
was a powerful fighting force. But luckily for the
Greeks, the uncouth barons from the western woods
were like children before the riches of Constantinople
and the grandeur of the Emperor.

Alexios Komnenos welcomed the strangers to his city

—an elegant, sophisticated figure in purple mantle and tunic of cloth-of-gold. His high-peaked hat was trimmed with fur and jewels; his reddish beard was full and richly curled. The mechanical birds sang; and his throne rose slowly in the air before the visitors' startled gaze.

The mouths of the barons hung open before such splendor. They thought they were in the presence of a deity.

Alexios had to be artful. He disliked these upstarts from the West. He didn't like their shaven faces or their smell of horses. He distrusted them. But he needed their help against the encroaching Turks. So he cajoled, flattered, bribed, made promises, and finally got this contingent of fighters also off to the Asiatic side of the Bosporus.

This time the excursion served some purpose. There was no massacre. The Turks fell back behind the advancing crusaders; and right behind the crusaders was Alexios, ready to claim his share in the spoils. In this way and without the loss of any of his own fighting men, he regained much of the territory that had before seemed hopelessly lost to the Turks.

From now on, for over two hundred years, crusade after crusade merged into one continuing movement from West to East, and back again.

One crusade conquered most of Asia Minor and captured the Holy City of Jerusalem. But the crusaders were unable to hold it. Toughened in the cold damp climate of Europe, these hardy warriors were soon weakened by soft living in the East. Mysterious veiled women, spiced Syrian dishes, the warm seductive climate relaxed them. All the fight slowly trickled out of their veins.

The Turks bided their time. Three-quarters of a century passed. Then rose Saladin, greatest of Turkish Sultans. In 1187 he retook Jerusalem. One by one after that, the other cities fell to the Turks; and soon all the East, from the Tigris to the Nile, was again firmly back in the hands of the infidel.

By this time the Western world was completely disillusioned as to the true spirit of the Crusades. The Papacy would no longer take any part in them. They were entirely in the hands of politicians and traders. The name "Crusade" was only a cover for money greed. Far from trying to oust the infidel, the Crusaders now tried to do business with them.

11

THE CATASTROPHE OF THE
FOURTH CRUSADE

The Fourth Crusade is of vital importance to the story of Constantinople. The immediate circumstances that touched it off are somewhat confusing, but the final outcome is starkly clear.

In the year 1202 the reigning emperor of Constantinople, Isaac Angelos, was deposed; and a usurper became emperor. Whereupon, the son of Isaac Angelos, in order to restore his father to the throne, made a journey to Europe to urge the Latins to come to his father's aid. He promised a large sum of money should his father be restored, also an army to help the Europeans reconquer the Holy Land and a permanent force to defend it.

The fighting dukes and barons jumped at the chance for another adventure. In Venice, Dandolo, the treacherous ninety-year-old Doge, rubbed his hands in glee. The Venetians needed more and more ports in the East for their thriving trade. Here was their chance!

The Crusaders had to use Venetian ships to make their trip across the sea, and the Venetian mariners saw to it that they landed directly in the heart of the Byzantine Empire, not in the Holy Land as many of the Crusaders desired.

A fleet of Venetian vessels with forty thousand strong-armed men arrived at the gates of the city of Constantinople. They threw out the new emperor, dragged old Isaac Angelos, now blind, out of prison, put him on the throne, and then waited for their promised reward.

For five months they waited. The son of Isaac could find no money and no men. But the Westerners stayed on and continued to press their demands. Inside and outside the walls they stayed—hard-fisted, hard-drinking Latins, while the Greeks, contained in their own walls, writhed with impatience and annoyance.

Starting with mutual dislike and distrust, the relations between the idling sailors, soldiers and roisterers, and the bitterly harassed Greeks became unbearable. They reached a climax when Isaac and his unfortunate son, now desperate for money and men with which to buy off their ill-chosen allies, tried to get hold of the church treasure. This was the end as far as the Greek people were concerned. They would stand for no more. In unabated fury they took out their indignation on the Latins. Every Westerner within the gates was slaughtered; Isaac died in terror; his son was strangled; and an officer of the army was proclaimed emperor.

Taking advantage of the chaos and urged on by Dandolo, the Crusaders now attacked the disorganized, undisciplined city.

The land walls held out. And the people of Constantinople were able to hold off the attackers until the Venetian ships found a spot under the sea wall where the men could climb up on the ramparts. In this way, a few were able to enter the city and open up the gates to let the waiting soldiery pour in.

The newly chosen officer-emperor fled and so did about two-thirds of the inhabitants of the city. This was on April 12, 1204.

For three days the Latins pillaged the city. Mighty Constantinople was sacked and destroyed. From his throne in Italy, Pope Innocent III denounced his own people who were thus betraying any possibility of friendship between the East and West. "Unity is now forever impossible," said the Pope.

The Crusaders had long since forgotten the Holy Land and their sacred vows. They plundered the churches and stabled their horses in Sancta Sophia. Convents were the scenes of orgies. Priests were tortured.

The Latins destroyed all that was beautiful. Ancient Greek statues were torn from their pedestals. Whole libraries were burned in the campfires. The tombs of the emperors were stripped of their metal. In the Hippodrome the Crusaders shattered the marbles with battle-ax and hammer and melted down the priceless bronzes to make copper money. It was at this time that the famous four horses were carried off to Venice.

The conquerors drove their supply wagons into the Blachernae Palace. That is why the room where we first saw Emperor Constantine Paleologus was despoiled of its treasure, why the floors were rutted and the walls bare.

Then the Crusaders set a fire which burned for eight days and nights and stretched over a territory two and a half miles wide. That is how the most magnificent city of the world was laid low.

No Turks that ever took a city before or after made such ruin as these French, Italian and Flemish marauders made of Christian Constantinople. Three days of pitiless bestiality and pillage were stamped forever into the memories of the Orthodox East.

Forty years later the Greeks rallied. With the help of the Genoese, who wanted to get even with their rivals, the Venetians, they retook the nearby cities in Asia Minor. And in 1261, under Emperor Michael VIII, they managed to get back into Constantinople. But nothing could ever restore the empire to its former greatness. Exhausted and impoverished by plunder, Constantinople was like an old woman. The Venetians, who had robbed her of her shipping, her trade and her industries, stayed on in the nearby islands, many actually in the city itself. The Genoese, who helped the Greeks regain their city, settled down in Galata, only a short row across the Golden Horn, and made it a city of their own. Constantinople had forever lost her glory.

This event marked the end of the Crusades in that part of the world. All Asia was now lost to the West. Except for irreparable devastation, the Crusaders might never have been there. After two and a half centuries, Europe did not retain one foot of the land she had fought for. Moreover, the eastward movement, begun in the eleventh century with the First Crusade, had begun to undermine the Christian empire of the East. The Fourth Crusade pounded it well-nigh out of existence.

The political adventurers who dismantled the Empire in 1204 were directly responsible for the fall of Constantinople 200 years later, and for the end of Christianity in the East.

12

THE FINAL ENEMY APPEARS

If the Latins and the Greeks, the East and the West, had united against the infidel, they might have subdued him. But East and West distrusted each other more than they distrusted the enemy. And now, when it was too late, a fresh force was rising in Asia that would quicken the weakening pulse of Mohammedanism.

Genghis Khan, the scourge of Asia, was on the rampage. Just about the time that the Latins were occupy-

ing Constantinople, the Mongol started on his terrifying stampede. Westward across the plains of Asia he
drove his hordes of horsemen, and on into Asia Minor.
The world is still aghast at the tales of terror and brutality. But our concern is the effect of Genghis Khan on
one particular tribe only.

This time it was Asiatics against Asiatics.

Like a mighty snowball, the Mongol hordes gathered tribe after tribe on their surge westward, adding the strong men of the tribes to their fighting force,
making slaves of the others. But always ahead of
them, still unconquered, galloped one swift-riding
tribe that had never been subdued. Women, children,
old men, slaves, cattle, a whole nation of people, were
fleeing together, protected by a band of warriors.
These were a new tribe of Turks. With the Mongols
close behind them, they crossed the Euphrates River
westward.

Such were the pioneers from whom sprang the strong
and capable nation of Ottoman Turks.

They got their name from their leader, Osman, a
warrior chief with flaming eyes and flowing beard,
a man of muscular beauty, worthy to be called the
Father of his Country. Riding across the plain, his long
wool cloak flying loose from his shoulders, sleeves
empty that his arms might be free, pantaloons wide,
feet bare, he was the ideal figure of the fighting Turk.

Once Osman had a dream. He dreamed of a mighty

tree which sheltered a large part of the world. Under it stood four mountain ranges, and from its roots gushed four great rivers: the Tigris, the Euphrates, the Danube and the Nile. Over the rivers and the mountains Osman heard the muezzin call to prayer. To him this meant that all these lands would one day be Moslem. When a strong wind rose—still in his dream— he saw that all the leaves of the tree pointed toward Constantinople.

Osman took the title of Sultan, which means Absolute Ruler, in 1300. He made the horsetail his military standard, which only a commander of high rank—a Pasha—could wear. Whether Osman had the dream or whether it was a minstrel's tale, we *do* know that with him started a line of Turkish sultans who ruled those same lands in the Mohammedan faith from that day down to our own time.

In 1326 the Ottoman Turks captured Brusa, the largest Christian city in Asia Minor; and from it they raided settlement after settlement until the entire Asiatic coast of the Marmora and the Bosporus was Turkish.

But Asia was not enough. The Ottomans next crossed the Hellespont and fought their way north through the region we know as the Balkans. There they made Adrianople (Edirne), next to Constantinople the most powerful city in the Empire, their European capital.

Like a mighty snowball the Mongol hordes surged westward.

head of them, still unconquered, rode a new tribe of Turks.

The Ottoman Empire now closed in toward Constantinople both on the north and on the south.

The Greeks in their desperation tried to bargain. They proposed marriages between emperors' daughters and sultans' sons. Things went so far that at one point an emperor's son conspired with a sultan's son to dethrone both their fathers. But the sultan heard of the plot and put his son to death, and the emperor blinded his.

It was too late to "make a deal." There was still no declared war between the two peoples. It was deliberate, powerful encroachment. After each Turkish victory the people of Constantinople listened fearfully for the thunderous approach of hoofbeats.

In the year 1402, they heard them.

The sultan of the Ottomans was then Bayezid, called "Lightning" because of the swift deadliness of his striking power.

With a decade of conquest behind him, Bayezid now laid plans for an attack on the Queen City. The emperor tried to buy him off by paying tribute, by permitting him to erect a mosque in his holy Orthodox Catholic city. But "Lightning" only laughed.

This was just fifty years before our actual story opens. Phranza, an elderly man, remembered it from his childhood. He remembered the terror in the city, the imminence of total disaster.

And then—just before the blow fell—on the very eve

of probable annihilation—Constantinople was miraculously saved. It was saved, not by Christian aid, but by another savage scourge from the East.

Timur, the Tartar, called Tamburlaine, was a descendant of Genghis Khan and an even more terrifying figure. In the middle of the fourteenth century, Timur set out from Samarcand in Asia to conquer the world. He spread out in every direction, burning, massacring, enslaving—in Persia, Russia, Siberia, China, India. Now his myriads of horsemen were coming over into Asia Minor.

Timur was a white-haired man, old and lame and gnarled. But he frightened the world. "Never to repent, never to regret," was his watchword. Even in that day of bloodshed and torture, his cruelty stood out as the ultimate.

Bayezid boasted that he was ready to meet Timur. And meet him he did, with 120,000 men against Timur's 300,000, plus thirty-two Indian elephants which terrified the Turkish horses. Surrounded by his guard, Bayezid fought until every man of them was slaughtered. Then when he tried himself to escape, his horse fell and the Mongols dragged him in triumph to Timur.

For eight months "Lightning," the hitherto indomitable Sultan Bayezid, was led from city to city in an iron cage. In every triumphal procession he was there for all to see.

After eight months Bayezid died. The Ottoman

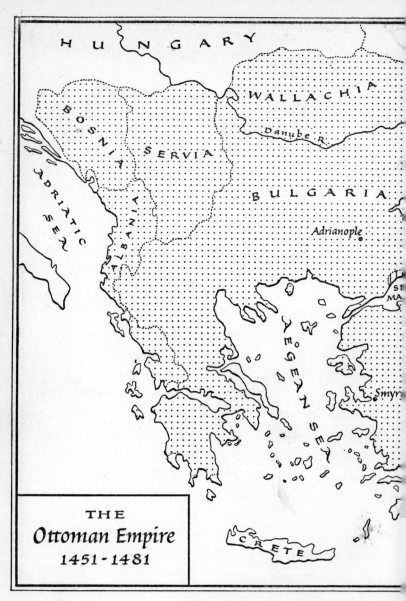

HUNGARY

WALLACHIA

BOSNIA

SERVIA

Danube R.

BULGARIA

ADRIATIC SEA

ALBANIA

Adrianople

AEGEAN SEA

ST
MA

Smyr

CRETE

THE
Ottoman Empire
1451 - 1481

By 1451 the Byzantine Empire inclu

the tiny area around Constantinople.

Turks were scattered. And the Mongols, like a pack of wolves, galloped back into Asia to raise further havoc in China. To them the Bayezid episode was only a large-scale raid.

Like the Crusaders, Timur accomplished nothing in Asia Minor except untold destruction. But because of his sudden appearance on the scene, Constantinople was given a new lease on life. By this unexpected turn in the affairs of man, instead of falling to Bayezid, the old city remained standing, trembling still, but alive within its walls.

For the moment, the Ottoman Turks were crushed.

But how did the Christians profit by this gift from the hand of fate?

While Timur was still fighting Bayezid, the Genoese in Galata (Constantinople's left hand, as it were) offered to ferry the defeated Turkish troops from Asia Minor, where they were trapped, to the mainland of Europe. The Genoese did it for a good price. Whereupon the Venetians, not to be outdone where money was concerned, competed for the same trade. They ferried still more Turks. And so, it must be admitted, did many of the money-minded Greeks in Constantinople itself.

In this way much of the Ottoman army was rescued.

Out of the crippled remnants a new sultan emerged, Mohammed I, who by his cool-headedness and moderation, restored the Turkish morale. Quietly and systematically he reorganized the army and brought

84

courage back to his people. In forty years he and his successors rebuilt the Ottoman nation. They recovered most of the territory lost in Asia Minor and prepared once more—under the guidance of Mohammed's formidable grandson—to attack Constantinople.

The grandson was Mohammed II, ambitious, cruel, crafty, treacherous—yet one of the great generals of the world, ranking in military history with Napoleon and Alexander.

This was the man from whom Khalil Pasha had come when the Emperor Constantine Paleologus received him.

The Sultan who preceded Mohammed II, his father Murad, had been a friend of the Greeks. That is to say, he had not been their enemy. He was busy fighting in the Balkans; he was building up his nation from the depredations of Timur; he had no time for Constantinople.

But Mohammed II, when he looked south from his capital at Adrianople, had a gleam in his eye. One year after he became sultan, he started work on Romeli Hissar, the fort on the Bosporus just six miles above Constantinople, the dream city of all Moslems. "The tribe that wins Constantinople wins paradise."

The early Mohammedan Arabs had tried to take Constantinople. The Seljuk Turks had tried. The Latins had only partially succeeded. Now. . . .

13

THE GREEKS PREPARE

There was little sleep for the Emperor Constantine on the night of Khalil Pasha's visit. At dawn he knelt once more before his ikon and again gazed out over the city. Pale light softened the dome of Sancta Sophia, and the water of the Golden Horn looked metallic in its stillness.

It was early when he called to his side the two

members of his government whom, next to Phranza, he trusted most.

Seated on his throne in Blachernae Palace, his back straight and his head high, he gave these men their formal instructions. Bearing the banner of the city, and wearing their most sumptuous robes of velvet and fur, the two ambassadors were to make the 150-mile journey to Adrianople to call upon the Sultan Mohammed. In the name of the Emperor, they were to protest the Sultan's proposal to build a fort. By proposing such a project the Sultan was breaking a treaty made by his father, which stated that no fortifications would be built by the Turks on the European shore of the Bosporus.

The Emperor had no illusions. He fully understood the Sultan's move. He knew that the mere breaking of a treaty would not stop the comet's course, that no threat of his could touch that driving force. Mohammed's plan to surround the city and starve it—always the first step in a siege—was devastatingly clear.

But Constantine's pride and his position as leader of his people demanded a diplomatic protest.

He had no hope of receiving a favorable reply; and when his ambassadors returned after a week, his worst fears were confirmed.

Mohammed had shrugged his shoulders and flatly denied that he was breaking a treaty. He was a man of peace, he said, and was acting for his troops' pro-

tection, not for war. Then his eyes sharpened. If the
Emperor were looking for trouble, that was another
matter! He was ready! What was more, if these two
returned with any more messages, he would have them
flayed alive! . . . So he told the noble Greek ambassadors.

The fortress of Romeli Hissar, only six miles up the
Bosporus, begun in March, was finished in August, a
little over five months later. It was a tremendous feat
of building which Mohammed himself superintended.
He let nothing stand in the way of his ambition. As
Khalil Pasha told the Emperor, a thousand master-
builders were brought from Asia; and for each of them
there were four masons and countless common workmen. Each day a certain measure of work to be done
was marked out, and woe to the workmen who did not
finish it. Mohammed kept constant watch. Every
night, if the work measured up, there were gifts. If not,
the lash.

The fort was triangular. Its stone walls were 22 feet
thick, and the towers, built at the three angles, were
30 feet thick. After 500 years it still stands at a turn of
the river and probably will be standing after another
500.

For supports Mohammed ruthlessly sent his men to
a nearby village to pull down the marble pillars and
the altar of the church; and when the Greeks put up

a fight at such blasphemy, they were slain on the spot—martyrs to the cause. When his men needed pasturage for their horses and mules, they used the farmers' fields and gardens. Finding Turkish mules and horses turned loose in their fields of ripe corn, the farmers rushed on the Turks and a bloody fight ensued. Many on both sides were killed. By way of punishment Mohammed had the whole village exterminated.

Emperor Constantine was broken-hearted at these outrages committed against his innocent people. A man may seem weak because he is kind or reasonable. Constantine was a kind and a reasonable man. But he was not weak. He was firm of purpose and brave in its execution. His patience had been stretched as far as it would go.

"We shall send troops to destroy this fort and its infidel builders!" he declared, his voice hot with righteous indignation.

But the monk Gennadius, speaking for the church, begged him not to invite war. Representatives of the people appealed to him not to antagonize the hostile Turks. And Constantine bitterly contained himself.

When the fort was completed, however, he sent his last message to Mohammed. "Since neither oaths, nor entreaty, nor submission can secure peace," he said, "pursue your impious warfare. My trust is in God alone! If it should please Him to soften your heart, I shall rejoice in the happy change; if He delivers the city into your hands, I submit without a murmur to His holy will. *But until the Judge of the earth shall pronounce between us, it is my duty to live and die in the defense of my people."*

He ordered the gates of the city closed: from this day on no Turk could enter Constantinople.

Using this as a cause, Mohammed formally declared war.

The bell had tolled. No one was fooling anyone any longer. It was the end of appeasement.

But the cold war continued.

All through the winter that followed, the two monarchs prepared feverishly for the coming clash.

The Emperor was in command of a city that was tired and old and of a people who through long centuries of peace and security had become unused to war. They were not the frivolous, luxury-loving people of the past. All profligacy and extravagance had vanished with the Fourth Crusade. But they had little initiative. They were sober, industrious and unimaginative—people who paid their heavy taxes and sent their boys as a matter of course into the army, workmen who did their jobs and then enjoyed a flagon of bitter resin wine at the wineshop. Having lived so many generations under an absolute monarchy where they had no say in affairs, they were as unused to politics as they were to war. One could not look for ideas or heroics among these citizens.

The bulk of the fighting men had formerly come from the provinces. But now that Asia Minor had fallen to the Turks, the supply of the Emperor's best men was cut off.

His officer material, largely the nobles, had had very little training. They, too, had been content and comfortable. Their energy had long since dried out. They were not wanting in courage; but they were without specific abilities, incapable of planning a campaign, or getting outside help.

The deepest concern of all the people of Constantinople—aristocrats and common people alike—was religion. Ironically this weakened their fighting cause. The clergy and the monks, like the others, felt secure. They had been idle too long, safe too long, ruled too long. Where the nobles believed resistance would be hopeless, the clergy looked for a miracle.

The burden of war fell squarely on the shoulders of Constantine. For the next six months during every waking hour he did all in his power to prepare his cumbersome city and its lethargic people for the struggle to come. He became leader both in planning and in fighting, an inspired example of devotion and self-sacrifice.

Unfortunately, Constantine's first public act of preparation, which grew out of his desperate need, met with sullen disapproval. On the 12th of December, a few months after the walls of Romeli Hissar were finished, the Emperor performed a ceremonious religious rite that cost him the support of many of his people. He invited the Roman Catholic Cardinal, Cardinal Isidore, to say Mass in the church of Sancta Sophia. The Mass was performed according to the ritual of the Roman Catholic, not the Greek Catholic, church. The Emperor attended and received Holy Communion from the hand of the Latin.

Now the Emperor Constantine was as devout a communicant of the Greek Orthodox church as there was in Constantinople. This act seemed as sacrilegious to him as it did to his people. He imagined the mighty figure of Christ frowning down upon him from His golden dome. But he sacrificed his personal emotions for what he believed to be the people's good.

And what did he gain?

To begin with, this was an act of diplomacy. Six months earlier, at the very first warning from Khalil Pasha, Constantine had begun to plan his campaign. Because his fighting forces were so small, he knew that he must have outside aid, and in order to get this aid he appealed to the West—which meant the world of the Roman Catholic church. *There must be peace between the two great Christian Catholic churches* if the infidel were to be beaten. Constantine therefore sent off two ambassadors to the Vatican.

For four hundred years the popes of Rome had sought unity between the two churches. Now for the first time a Greek emperor was offering them that unity —with a proviso that in return he receive a fighting force to help conquer the Turks.

The men of the Vatican looked upon the ambassadors with a cool eye. The old-time distrust of the Greeks was still there. But they figured that it could do no harm to send a representative. That is how, in six months' time, Cardinal Isidore arrived with a retinue of priests and soldiers to the number of fifty. News of his coming had leaked out, and the people were angry even before he arrived.

So in December when the Latin Cardinal said Mass in Sancta Sophia and the Emperor received communion from his hands, the Greeks cried out that they had been betrayed. When the Pope's name was mentioned in the liturgy of the Mass, they shouted their disapproval.

After this fateful church service, the scandalized crowds wandered unhappily through the streets. They denounced the Latins, denounced the union of the churches, and (secretly) denounced their own Emperor. Grand Duke Notaros, the noble first in rank under the Emperor, encouraged the angry people. He, too, and a certain clique of the nobility were deeply hostile to unity. "Better the turban of Mohammed than a cardinal's red hat!" he was quoted as saying. The slogan passed from lip to lip.

The magnificent church of Sancta Sophia was now deserted as if polluted by the plague. The great throngs that used to gather there found their way instead to the wine taverns. Instead of praying, they stood on street corners listening to the preaching of superstitious monks.

"An angel of the Lord will protect you," cried these men of the church. "Infidel troops may enter the city, but when they do, a great blue angel will descend from heaven and banish them!"

In their apathy, the people waited for a miracle.

In the very presence of a powerful enemy, religion had divided the people of Constantinople.

All this for the aid of fifty men!

Manpower was the Emperor's greatest need.

Constantine was a thorough man and a good organizer in spite of the gentleness of his nature. He left no stone unturned that might help the cause. He had to know to the last man how many men he could call upon to fight. Every house was visited, every man questioned as to his ability and his willingness to bear arms in defense of his city when the time came.

This investigation the Emperor had put into the hands of trusted Phranza. Now Phranza came with the figures. They were not good. *Out of a population of roughly 100,000, only 4970 expressed themselves as willing and able to fight! At least 35,000 men of military age lived in the city,* protected and cared for by their Emperor. *But they held back,* some of them because of cowardice, others because they had been roused to anger by their Emperor's gesture toward Rome.

Of the nobles, many had already left the city, fearful of a siege. Most of those who remained were deeply loyal and ready to fight to the end. Others refused to declare themselves—like Duke Notaros. They wanted to be on the spot, ready to join the victorious side. They had their wives hide their riches and let the poor of the city go hungry. In fact, Phranza reckoned that if the nobles would give up their hidden treasures to the government, whole armies of mercenaries could be hired in the city's defense.

(In those days no European country had a standing army. When war was imminent, mercenaries were hired to do the fighting—professional soldiers of whatever nationality was available, who received higher wages than the men of the country itself who were fighting for a cause.)

The Emperor's face tightened when he heard Phranza's report: in the whole magnificent city, only a handful who cared enough to fight for the protection of their wives and children and homes!

"It shall be a secret between us!" he whispered. And a secret it remained until four years after the siege of Constantinople when Phranza himself wrote the story of how his Emperor tried to save the city.

On the credit side, the Genoese in Galata offered Constantine a band of 4000 fighting men, not so much to help out the Greeks as to get ahead of the Venetians in case of victory. These, of course, were mercenaries.

The greatest single asset to the defenders came in the person of John Giustiniani, a Genoese captain who arrived by ship in January, 1453. Giustiniani was a man of powerful strength and great size, a soldier of fortune of noble birth, who had come of his own accord to fight for the Emperor's cause. With him he had brought 700 fighting men, of whom 400 were swaggering, experienced Genoese cavalry soldiers with shining breastplates.

If a heavenly host had descended upon him, the Emperor could not have been more relieved. He at once made Giustiniani commander in chief, and offered him, as a reward when the war was over, the beautiful island of Lesbos. "He is a good man," he told Phranza soberly. "I shall be able to work with him."

"It's his profession," said Phranza cynically. "He fights for his own ends."

"He is dependable," the Emperor reiterated with conviction. "I expect the best of Giustiniani."

Besides the Galata Genoese and Guistiniani's imported men, there were some 1600 Venetians and other Westerners who had been living in Constantinople for many generations. This was their war as well as the Greeks', and when the test came, many of them proved to be heroes.

The Emperor's next step was to call in two foreigners of great skill who were well known in the city. Johann Grant, a clever German miner, came at once and offered his services. But Urbann, the Hungarian, an artillery expert, was found to have deserted to the Turks.

"Not enough pay," Grant told the Emperor gruffly. He spoke Greek easily because he had lived in the city so long. "Urbann's a big man, and he likes to eat. Now he works for the infidel, who pays with gold or the whip, as it pleases him."

"For Urbann it will be gold," murmured the Emperor. Urbann had long ago told him his idea for a huge cannon, but Constantinople in all its coffers had not enough money to pay for such a cannon as Urbann dreamed of.

The nights were cold and the Emperor allowed no heat in the Blachernae Palace. Like many modern houses it was heated through its floors. But now the wood usually used for fires beneath the floors was sent to the bakeries to bake bread. Food was collected from every possible source and stored through the winter months for whatever calamity spring might bring.

To the handful of willing fighters, the Emperor sent crossbows, muskets and shields from the arsenal.

Out in the harbor a strong new chain was forged, a Boom, supported on floats of massive timbers. It was said that its links of iron were as big as Giustiniani's leg. The Boom was to be drawn across the mouth of the Golden Horn when the time came. Now every ship that entered the harbor was held to do its share of public service. "We need every ship and every cargo," declared the Emperor.

Thus six months went by in sleepless preparation. The people were sullen. Phranza was gloomy. The Grand Duke Notaros was aloof. Every day the Emperor conferred with Giustiniani and Johann Grant on military defense.

Constantinople still had one powerful reservoir of strength. That was her walls. Built in the fifth century, repaired and rebuilt and strengthened through succeeding centuries, these walls were now the limits of the Byzantine Empire. But they were seemingly impregnable limits, fourteen miles of masonry, three layers deep. They were stronger and better fortified than any city walls in Europe. The world still believed that they could never fall.

The walls were in three sections—on the west or landward side, on the Sea of Marmora, and on the side of the Golden Horn.

The landward walls ran from the Blachernae Palace to the Sea of Marmora, a distance of about six miles. The Inner Wall of this section, called the Great Wall, was from 40 to 70 feet high, and from 12 to over 36 feet thick, built of solid stone and buttressed by many towers. The Outer Wall, also with towers, was lower than the Great Wall. Between the two was a 50-foot platform where soldiers could concentrate should the Outer Wall be breached. This was where the final hand-to-hand fighting would take place.

Beyond the Outer Wall lay the moat, 60 to 70 feet wide, and in no place less than 30 feet deep. Its drawbridges were removed entirely in time of siege, and its walls were built of stone so smooth and sheer as to allow no foothold. Water pipes were hidden in the moat which could be used to flood it or to carry water in to the besieged, as was needed. Information about these pipes was a state secret which only a trusted few shared with the Emperor.

Into these powerful landward walls were built seven gates, all of which figure dramatically in the tragic story about to unfold.

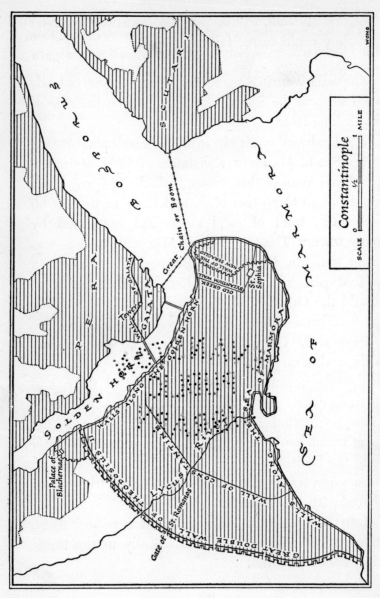

Map showing the fortifications of Constantinople during the siege of 1453.

The walls on the Sea of Marmora were lower than the landward walls because the sea itself was a natural fortification. And on the Golden Horn side, they were still lower. Because of the massive Boom to protect the harbor entrance, a strong wall here was considered unnecessary.

These then were the walls.

In the days before cannon, consider what it meant to try to defy them. First, there was the moat—actually a broad deep river to cross, with high walls of smooth rock.

Should any device be erected by which to cross the moat and surmount the wall, the attackers would next be faced by the Outer Wall.

Should battering rams be built that could break through this wall, or ladders that could scale it, behind it stood the fighting forces of the defenders assembled and waiting.

Last of all the invader would come up against the Inner Wall, the strongest single defense ever built by man. For more than a thousand years it had held back waves upon waves of fighting men. . . .

Mohammed II was far from sure of victory.

14

THE TURKS PREPARE

It was now April, 1453. Mohammed's silken tent of red and gold was pitched on a hill opposite the Gate of St. Romanos, only a mile and a half away from the walls and close enough for the Emperor to see from Blachernae Palace.

Turkish troops were on the march—mounted warriors, companies of foot soldiers counting to a thousand men each, hordes of plunderers, slingers, archers, lancers. From the ramparts the people of Constantinople watched the massed formations streaming over the hills behind Galata, so lately trodden by caravans laden with food for the great city market. Now herds of cattle were being driven along behind the horsemen, ensuring the enemy's food supply for months to come.

By the tens of thousands the enemy came. In front rode the Turkish fighters, their red cloaks cutting a swathe across the pale spring green of the hillside, their curved scimitars shining in the sunlight. Behind them came the captive slaves, Serbs and Bulgars and Hungarians, who would be forced to fight. Then came the Christian mercenaries willing to fight with the infidel for the money he paid them.

Every day more came.

At intervals teams of oxen could be seen dragging the Turkish guns.

The Turkish army was encamping on the hills to the west of the city. Their tents extended all the way from the north end of the Golden Horn (near Blachernae Palace) to the Sea of Marmora. By day the rolling hills were dotted as far as the eye could see with men, slaves, horses, cattle. At night the red of their campfires was reflected on the low-hanging clouds—a semicircle of fire at which the people of the city gazed in horrible fascination. The Queen City was cut off from the outside world. No one could leave or enter.

Up the Bosporus at the new fort of Romeli Hissar every ship from the Black Sea laden with food for the city was held up. Guns were installed on the battlements which could throw balls of stone weighing up to 600 pounds. Should a ship resist, these guns were turned upon it. One Venetian ship which refused to comply was sunk with a single shot. The sailors of her crew escaped drowning but were picked up out of the water by Turks and brought before their commander. All thirty men were massacred, their bodies sawed in half. Their captain was impaled on a sword.

As it happened, this was the very captain with whom Phranza had sailed on his journey to the Black Sea only nine months before. It seemed like a hundred years; and the princess, waiting for her husband-to-be, was long since sadly forgotten.

But this particular brutality boomeranged on the Turks. The Venetians of Constantinople and the islands, previously in it only for the sport, now dedicated themselves wholeheartedly to the cause of the Greeks against Mohammed. It was now their war too!

The two nations about to face each other in battle were as fundamentally different as were the abodes of their leaders—the brightly striped silken tent of Mohammed, the old stone palace of the Emperor. The Turks were a young vigorous people, the Greeks were old and tired and lived in the past. They were dying spiritually.

The Turks were shepherds, warriors, vagabonds, thieves, grown overnight into an army of conquerors. Their habits were frugal, they drank no intoxicating liquor.

Militarily they were the finest soldiers in the world, trained in the strictest discipline. Implicit obedience to authority was demanded, and individuality was crushed in favor of the mass. It was the kind of training that made for a docile, good-tempered, patient, sober and heroic army. Only when stirred up by religious exhortation did the individuals among them become wild savages. And this burning incentive was reserved for the final stages of battle.

The core of Mohammed's army was the cavalry, called *Spahees*. In battle these horsemen wore chain armor and carried a curved scimitar, a long lance, and an iron-mounted baton which could be hurled. They were tireless horsemen. They often journeyed seventy to ninety miles between sunrise and sunset, loose horses following the troops so a rider could always have a change of mount if an animal were worn out or injured. A Turk could fight on foot, but his horse must be near by. When an infantry attack was unsuccessful, the Spahees covered the retreat of the attackers.

The officers of the Spahees were men of importance; their clothes were rich; their tents were elegant. But any one of them would throw back the sleeves of his rich furred cloak to fasten on a horse's shoe, which few Christian officers would be willing to do, even if they could.

Mohammed paid well the Christian mercenaries whom he employed, which poor Emperor Constantine could not afford to do. He also had skilled engineers, whom he paid better. Hence the defection of Urbann, the Hungarian. If any soldier, officer or man among them showed any mark of insolence or mutiny, there was always a Grand Vizier or Pasha near by to stick a sword into his back.

It was the Janizaries that made the Turkish army unique. These fanatical warriors, strange as it may seem, were born Christians. When the Turks captured Christian villages, they picked out the most robust and promising boys under fifteen and sent them to Asia for training. They lived with families of Turkish peasants and were educated in the Moslem faith. Well-treated and young, they soon forgot their actual parents or at any rate did not miss them. In fact, of all the Turkish army they were the most uncompromising toward conquered Christians.

The Janizaries were the Turkish "shock troops." They were hardened by every kind of military exercise, better fed and clothed than the rest of the army. "Let them be called *Janizaries* (new soldiers); let their countenance be always bright; their hands victorious, their swords sharp; let their swords hang over the heads of the enemy, and wherever they go let them return with a happy face."

The Janizaries' training was not unlike that of the commandos of today. They had to do hard physical labor, dig, carry heavy weights, spend long periods on coarse and scanty food, perform feats of extraordinary strength and endurance. They must obey all commands blindly. When a young recruit was ready for his final nomination to a company, his initiation was a blow on the head from his captain that often threw him to the ground, stunned and bleeding.

When a Janizary walked among civilians, he was never allowed to loiter; he had to carry a white cane so that all would recognize him; in battle he wore a white cap. He had to be soldierly and modest.

No soldiery in the world has ever had the reputation for such fearlessness, such fighting ability, such devotion to their cause. At first the Janizaries numbered only about 6000; but by the time of Mohammed II, the number that faced Constantinople had been increased to 12,000. It was the Janizaries who were called up to finish off a victory. So great was their reputation that their mere appearance on the field of battle was enough to benumb and terrify the enemy.

To this vast army religion came before home, self or nation. At sundown every Moslem on that vast plain knelt down and prayed. The Sultan on his rug with his sword pointed toward Mecca prostrated himself many times. On Friday, the holy day of Islam, not a blow could be struck, either in battle or in preparation for battle. "Let the True Believers fight for the Religion of Allah. . . . For to whosoever fighteth for the Religion of Allah, whether he be slain or victorious, will surely be given a great reward." To the Moslem there was no surer way to be forgiven a life of sin than to die in battle and be transported straight to the golden fields of paradise.

To stir the soldiers to a state of religious frenzy on the night before a battle, the Sultans called in the dancing dervishes. These were a Moslem religious order, not unlike monks in the Christian churches. Their dance was performed according to a fixed ritual, and every turn and twist had a symbolic meaning.

In long black robes, with full wide skirts the better to whirl in, in turbans and little short jackets, the dervishes entered the army encampment in a long line, and moved slowly and undulatingly toward the soldiers awaiting them, tensely silent.

To the faint music of the tambourine, the leader commenced slowly to turn on the heel of his bare right foot. His head was bowed low over his right shoulder; his arms were extended; and his eyes half closed in ecstasy. A second dervish then began to circle in the same way, then another and another, until the entire line had joined in the dance. The whole world seemed to be twirling.

Faster and faster they revolved, their skirts spreading as they whirled until they stood at right angles from the body. In circle upon circle the dancers turned around one another, always faster and faster, but never an arm nor a skirt touching. . . . Their faces were transformed. They were seized with delirium. For an hour and a half they danced, circles around circle, faster and faster and still faster. They forgot the earth beneath them. They thought only of Allah. . . .

By this time the soldiers were stirred to madness. They were ready to commit any atrocity to win for Allah—massacre the wounded, hack corpses, chop off hands.

Such was the army of the Sultan: 12,000 Janizaries, 20,000 Spahees, 100,000 infantry, and uncounted hordes of slaves and herdsmen who answered the trumpet call to salvation. In all, Phranza had reckoned that there were 250,000 of the enemy, opposing 7000 or 8000 Christians, with sixteen miles of wall to defend!

Behind the army came the heavy Turkish guns. All day long, teams of oxen came over the hill behind Galata, dragging the cannon which the Turks set up opposite the landward walls. They extended in a formidable line the full length of the walls, with the heaviest artillery massed at four strategic points.

To show his disdain, the Emperor ordered 1000 men from the ships in the harbor, mostly Venetians, to assemble on the walls. There, to the beat of drums and the whistle of fife, flying their banner with its Lions of St. Mark, they marched crisply back and forth the length of the landward walls.

It was only show, yet Mohammed from his hillside viewed them uneasily.

Mohammed was far from certain of victory. *Was he destined to be the one man who could break through those impregnable walls? Or would he, like the others, be vanquished?*

In his silken tent the Sultan could not sleep. The only sounds on the hillside where he was encamped were the occasional whinny of a horse and the subdued regular tread of the guard. Unlike most of his predecessors, Mohammed was a cultivated man. But now the book beside his couch lay opened, face down. He was too uneasy to read.

Impatiently he rose from his bed and commanded the instant presence of his prime vizier, Khalil Pasha.

When Khalil Pasha got the call, he trembled inwardly. He kissed his wife and children as for a long farewell. After all, he had warned the Christians twice six months ago, and six months before that. He had told them to prepare, and they had prepared. This was treason. He liked his Christian friends. Yet he had taken pay from them. This was avarice.

But once Khalil Pasha had bowed himself into the presence of his Sultan, his manner was outwardly calm.

As was customary for any Turkish subject appearing before his sovereign, Khalil Pasha brought a gift. He had filled a cup with gold and laid it at the young Sultan's feet.

Mohammed acknowledged the gift with a bow. Usually he greeted his grand vizier with a laugh and a good-natured jibe, for Mohammed was a jovial young man. But tonight he was deadly serious. "I ask a far greater present of you, my venerable counselor," he cried.

The vizier gazed at his prince through lowered lashes.

"I ask Constantinople!"

He was demanding the ultimate. But it was *not* personal. So weakened with relief that he could scarcely stand, Khalil Pasha yet managed to reply with suavity. "The same God who has already given thee so large a portion of the empire, Sire," he said, "will not deny you now the one remaining city. And I myself," he added sanctimoniously, "with the rest of thy faithful slaves, will gladly sacrifice our lives and fortunes in thy cause."

111

Mohammed relaxed. He had only wanted reassurance!

Other nights the Sultan went out in disguise among his soldiers to hear what was being said among them. Even if one recognized him, he would dare not admit it.

He argued with his generals and questioned his engineers. Where should he assault the walls? Where should he spring his mines? At what spot could he raise scaling ladders? If there was a weak spot, where was it?

Months ago he had conferred with Urbann, deserter from the Emperor. "Could Urbann cast a cannon capable of throwing a ball of stone big enough to batter the walls of Constantinople?" Mohammed had asked.

When Urbann convinced him that such a cannon could be created, the Sultan built a foundry in Adrianople under Urbann's directions, bought the necessary quantities of metal, and by the end of three months saw a piece of brass ordnance so stupendous in size as to defy belief. This deadly monster was already on its way south.

15

THE SIEGE

As the Turks slowly encircled Constantinople, tension increased within the walls.

When would the blow fall? the people asked one another—women in the market place, men in the wineshop. *Would it be today—tomorrow? Would they have a home tomorrow?*

All through the winter the nerves of the nation were on edge.

Yet life went on. The men still went to work. Shops remained open, and traders still bargained in the bazaar. The women kept their households going as best they could. Clothes wore out and had to be mended. Children played in the doorways of the narrow houses.

Food became scarce. The ships from the west with promised grain had not come. Only the soldiers could have meat, and for them there was very little. Bread was distributed equally among all, but the Emperor asked that the old give some of their share to the young who must bear the greatest part of the burden.

The weak among the people trembled in fear. The greedy hid their riches. The traitors were plotting which master they would best follow when the time came for a choice.

But the small core of fighters was eager for battle. As the Turks continued to pour into their encampment, the resistance tightened. The Venetian mercenaries, whose work it was to guard Blachernae Palace, became more debonair and daredevil as danger grew closer. The Genoese, best fighters of them all, waited impatiently. The Greeks who were faithful were willing and ready to die for Emperor and Church. They girded themselves daily for death.

No longer did the Emperor sit on his throne in Blachernae Palace. Every day saw him on horseback, riding the length of the walls, inspecting the prepa-

114

rations for siege, encouraging the men at their work.

Captain Giustiniani and Johann Grant rode with him examining the bulwarks.

"The greatest danger—the weakest spot—it is here!" Giustiniani said, pointing to the foundations of the wall between the Gate of St. Romanos and the palace of Blachernae. Far below it the Lycus River made an underground passage.

Johann Grant agreed. "Here it *must* be reinforced," he said.

To get together the money for men and material strained the Emperor's feeble resources to the last penny. No one in the world of that day could have believed it possible that the empire of Constantinople could not afford to mend its walls. It would have been inconceivable that a city once so rich and so extravagant could scarcely pay its men's wages.

But this was an all-important undertaking, and the Emperor went about it to the exclusion of all other business. Saving something here, selling something there, taxing the people to the very limit, he finally, with Phranza's able help, succeeded in scraping together the sum of 70,000 gold byzants. Its sole purpose was the reinforcement of the walls—the last hope, as the experts saw it, of the city's survival. Not one byzant was to be used for any other cause.

The Emperor then called to him two men of the

church—two monks, Nicodemus of Rhodes and Manuel Jagaris.

In their black robes, faces pale in contrast to their brown curling beards, the two stood solemnly before him.

The Emperor raised one of three bags that lay on the table between him and his visitors. The bag clinked. "For four months," he told the monks, "we have saved and worked throughout Constantinople. We have collected the golden coins now contained in these bags. It is for our last defense against the infidel. We thereby give it in your charge as our most trustworthy custodians."

Exact instructions were given as to the steps to be taken in the care and use of the money; and then the monks, one carrying one bag, the other carrying two bags, backed slowly out of the room from the presence of their Emperor.

But the three bags of gold never fulfilled their destiny. Many months later, when the city had fallen into the hands of the enemy, some Turkish Janizaries, cleaning up the rubble, unearthed three bags of 70,000 gold byzants, hidden deep in a tower. The monks had never paid out the gold entrusted to them. Instead they had cached it away for themselves. The sector that was to have been fortified was the first to crumble. The men who worked on it were never paid.

On April 12th, the enemy guns started their bombardment on the landward walls. The cannon boomed and the foundations of the city shook with the vibration.

Through the previous weeks the people had watched the Turks gathering—as at a parade. In dreadful fascination they clung to the ramparts. Now panic seized them. They rushed away from the walls and slunk, moaning and crying, through the narrow streets. They flocked into Sancta Sophia, so lately scorned. They paraded with the image of the Virgin held aloft.

But the Virgin's eyes were closed to their selfish entreaties, and the thunderous roar of guns continued.

On the walls where the fighting men and their officers were directing the defense of the city, there was tension but no panic. Far from it! The defenders could not fire back because their ammunition was limited and must be saved for the day of still greater peril that they knew lay ahead. Moreover their own heavy cannon could never be used lest the force of its explosion shake and shatter the ancient walls on which it stood.

But there was plenty that the small band of fighters could do, and do it they did like men inspired. Now that the time for action had come, Greeks, Venetians, Genoese, were heroes to a man. The Emperor and his captain, Constantine and Giustiniani, were tireless. They never slept. Here, there, everywhere, they were present always, Giustiniani to direct, the Emperor to encourage.

All day long the Turkish guns continued to pound. Every day. All day. Large pieces of Outer Wall began to crumble and fall to the ground.

But at night the Greeks crept forth, crawled outside the walls, and all through the hours of darkness repaired the damage of the day. They lifted up the stones that had broken away and where they could, replaced them. They lashed mattresses to weak spots, bales of wool to lessen the blows, cowhides for further protection.

Each morning, at break of day, the Turks found the walls that they had demolished, again erect, apparently as strong as before.

Trying to divert the defenders, the Turks moved to the sea wall and there flung up a scaling ladder. But again the Greeks were ready for them. Boiling pitch and hot lead rained down on their heads, and Turks dropped screaming and burning into the sea.

When they tried to tunnel under the wall, Johann Grant detected the telltale sounds. Full speed he galloped to Blachernae Palace. "Come, Sire," he begged the Emperor. The two were comrades now. There was little ceremony between them.

The Emperor, already mounted, turned his horse's head and followed behind Grant over the rough stones. When they reached the Crooked Gate, between the palace and the Gate of St. Romanos on the landward walls, they stopped.

Johann Grant leaped from his horse and put his ear to the ground. "Listen!" he whispered, his wide German face red with excitement.

Sure enough, a muffled sound of digging could be heard. The German grinned at his companion and told him his plan.

Not waiting for night, the defenders shot enough sulfur fumes down into the laboriously dug tunnel to suffocate all that might be caught in it and any that would try to enter later.

The Turks tried in fourteen places to undermine the walls; but each time, and in each place, the Greeks foiled them—with sulfur, with stink pots, with fire, with water. Once they met, Turk and Greek, and fought hand-to-hand beneath the surface of the earth. But the enemy never succeeded in causing an explosion.

The defenders were valiant and alert. But the nights were getting shorter. The Outer Wall crumbled faster than the repairmen could close it up. The people within the city trembled as word came through to them. Instead of helping defend their city, they followed the monks. They hid in the churches.

By April 18th, six days after the bombardment started, a serious breach was made, and two towers fell.

This, Mohammed decided, was his chance, and he gave orders for an immediate assault on the city.

At nightfall on the eighteenth the Turkish infantry in their red fezzes, cuirassiers in armor, archers and lancers advanced. With long hooks fastened to their lances, they tore at the vine branches and cotton bales with which the Greeks had repaired the walls, then set them on fire. But the defenders at once put the fire out. Turkish soldiers tried to scale the wall, but Giustiniani and his men drove them back with heavy losses.

The cries of the wounded reached into the houses where the women prayed before their ikons.

No one slept as the battle raged.

In four hours of heavy night fighting, the Turks lost 200 men and Mohammed had to retire. In his anger he admitted defeat: *A Moslem army of hundreds of thousands was being held by a handful of inspired Christians.*

16

SHIPS TRIUMPHANT

The next clash came by sea. Of all the Turks' fighting force, the weakest by far was its navy. If Allah had given them the earth, he had left the sea to the Christians. The Turks were an inland desert people, unfamiliar with waterways, splendid on horseback but out of place on ships. This, however, did not deter Mohammed. He had the city well hemmed in by land. It was already near starvation, but rescue ships with food and men from the West could still defeat him.

To meet this possible emergency, Mohammed summoned a fleet of his own. From Egypt and Syria, from up the Bosporus, from any port where a ship could be hired for gold, he gathered together a fleet of vessels which by the time they were assembled, numbered 300. But what a fleet! All the vessels were small open boats except eighteen war galleys, and these were without guns and overcrowded with troops.

In ungainly disorder the enemy boats now began to converge around Constantinople. Through the Hellespont and down the Bosporus, in typical Turkish fashion they arrived with trumpets blaring, drums beating, men shouting. Once assembled they lay in a bulky crescent just outside the Boom at the entrance of the harbor.

Once more the people climbed up on the walls and silently watched as each boat came into position.

The imperial navy bottled up in the harbor was in a precarious state. Ten months earlier, when the Emperor realized that Mohammed meant war to the finish, he had begged ships and supplies from Genoa and Venice. He asked them in the cause of Christendom, and the ships had been duly promised him. That was June, 1452. Now it was April, 1453, and as yet no help had come.

Just at this point, when the hopes of the Christians

had reached their lowest depths, a new silhouette showed over the horizon.

Shading their eyes against the western sky, the Greeks watching from the walls saw five tall ships emerge out of the misty distance—one by one—ships with lofty poops and full-flown square sails.

The people shouted. Here at last were ships! They would be laden with corn! In their holds would be wine and oil! On their decks, soldiers and seasoned mariners! The citizens waved, shouted, threw up their caps, and held the children up to see. They peered into the distance looking for other ships to follow. But no more came.

Five ships against 300!

But the five big ships were manned by experienced Genoese and Venetians, and they advanced boldly toward the closed crescent of Turkish boats awaiting them.

It was learned later that the Christian ships had been delayed by adverse winds through all of March and much of April. It was not until the morning of April 20th that the impatient sailors at last saw the dome of Sancta Sophia against the pale sky of sunrise.

Now the winds were behind them, and with shouts of derision from all aboard, tossing spray in their speed, the five ships came straight on in deadly hostility.

Thousands of spectators watched from the shores.

From the walls of the city, from the European shore of Galata and the Asian shore of the Turks, Christian and infidel alike looked out upon the scene.

The Sultan, when he got the message, galloped two miles from his tent to the beach at the tip end of Galata.

The Christian ships were getting close. Sitting high in the water they had a great advantage over the smaller vessels, both in hurtling darts and javelins and in beating off any of the enemy stalwart enough to attempt to board them. And the experienced mariners were fully prepared for aggression or defense. Their armor could withstand the enemy arrows and small missiles. They had barrels of water to extinguish any fire from flaming torches. They had axes to chop off hands and to break heads of any who had the temerity to get anywhere near the decks. With maddening insolence they steered straight into the enemy fleet.

But now, with the sun well up, the wind dropped. This brought the big ships to a standstill, and the real fighting began.

The Turkish boats tried to surround them. But from the turrets on their masts the Genoese threw lances and shot arrows. From aloft on yards and bowsprits they dropped heavy stones on the low vessels alongside.

The results were disastrous. Shouts of joy rose from the city walls as boat after boat of the enemy overturned and sank, the men swimming wildly about at the mercy of Christian missiles. The sea was so covered with ships and struggling men that they could scarcely see the water.

For three hours the fight went on.

Mohammed, riding up and down on the beach, screamed imprecations. "Cowards! Fools!"

He yelled promises and rewards to those who would get aboard an enemy ship. He threatened deserters. In his fury he rode his horse straight into the sea, his long cloak trailing behind him on the water.

"Keep them out of the harbor," he shouted to his admiral, "or don't come back alive!"

The admiral did what he could. He ordered the men to board the enemy vessels at any cost. He ran his own galley directly into the side of an Italian transport.

But the Sultan's defeat was complete. It is said that that day he lost all 300 ships and 12,000 men including some of his best fighters. Though the admiral was badly wounded and had lost an eye, the Sultan deprived him of all his honors and possessions. His life was spared only because of the pleading of his men. But he was ignominiously beaten—stretched on the ground and beaten by slaves with a golden rod of great weight.

The Christians had not lost a man. By sunset the wind rose again. The sails filled and the five ships plowed their triumphant way through the debris of the enemy, to the Boom. Once inside the harbor they unloaded their food and wine and men and oil.

It was at this time, with the joy of victory in their hearts, that a little Greek brigantine set sail to search the seas for the other promised ships. Twelve brave men volunteered. Disguised as Turkish sailors and flying the red Turkish flag, they succeeded in getting through unmolested.

In the city the jubilation of the people knew no bounds. For the first time in six months, in their joy, the citizens of Constantinople were once more a united people.

It was a brilliant fight and could have been the turning point. The young Sultan, temperamental, high-charged, was discouraged. Mines couldn't win. Attack had failed. Ships had proved a calamity. He was ready to lift the siege on which he had worked day and night for a year, and retreat.

Khalil Pasha, his venerable counselor, still mindful of his friends, the Christians, was pleased. He seconded Mohammed's decision. It was obvious the city never could be taken, he argued, except by a double attack, one attack from the harbor and one from the land. But as the harbor of the Golden Horn was obviously inaccessible—had it not been proven so?—a successful attack was clearly impossible. The Boom was unbreakable and was now further guarded by the five strongly manned vessels whose demon strength they had just witnessed.

Khalil Pasha gazed through his eyelashes at his lord.

The young Sultan's finely cut features were twisted in an odd grimace—whether in anger and disappointment or in a vindictive smile, Khalil Pasha could not tell.

Perhaps in his deviousness the old man had given him an idea; perhaps in his secretive way Mohammed had already conceived of a way out. *The city could never be taken except by a double assault, one from the harbor as well as one from the land.*

The next day 100 cannon shots were fired around the Boom, some even on Galata. This was doubtless a feint to distract attention. Frightened though they were by the withering blasts, the people could not resist climbing the low harbor wall to see what new horror the enemy had concocted. But what they saw could not be the work of man! Only the powers of darkness could have accomplished this deadly miracle!

Over the hill behind Galata, in plain view of the palace of Blachernae and the walls of the city, they saw ships sailing over the land! Twenty, thirty, forty vessels they counted, one behind the other, sails wide, moving slowly—very slowly—but surely—*down the hill and into the harbor of the Golden Horn!* Forty, fifty, sixty. . . .

Mohammed's mad notion had worked. With the

swiftness that characterized him, he accomplished what he did in one night—though he may have been secretly planning it long before. No one knows. . . .

Runways of timbers oiled with the fat of sheep and oxen were put through Galata; and on them, the ships on rollers were pulled over the land. Some were drawn by buffaloes, some by men with pulleys. Two pilots were stationed fore and aft on each vessel, and the sails were unfurled to the winds.

As the ships moved over the land and down the hill, the Turks shouted in excitement and sang in triumph.

In one night eighty ships of thirty oars each were thus moved from the Bosporus at Romeli Hissar, cross country to the Golden Horn. It was strategy of a high order. For now the Sultan could force the Greeks to defend three instead of only two sides of their triangle; he had the Genoese of Galata in a position where they could give no aid to the beleaguered even if they would; and his own communications, between army encampment and Romeli Hissar, were immeasurably shortened.

Mohammed could never have accomplished such a superhuman feat without the help of the Genoese, who not only gave him permission for the runway to go through their city, but sold him rope and rollers and sheep fat.

Such was the enemy of Constantine—rich, powerful, resourceful. And such were his Christian neighbors—

disloyal, greedy, and in the long historical picture, incredibly foolish.

The Emperor and Giustiniani stood behind the parapets of the wall that overlooked the Golden Horn. It was the day after the Turkish ships had come overland.

Of all the wall around the city this section was lowest and thinnest. In fact originally there had been no wall, as the harbor had been considered protection enough. Under their very eyes, the Greeks now saw that safety violated. Infidel ships rocked easily in waters where enemy ships had never before penetrated.

"They must be destroyed!" muttered Giustiniani.

The quayside of Galata upon which he gazed was a scene of feverish animation. In the first light of day, the Turks had started to build a pontoon bridge to span the harbor from Galata to a point immediately beyond the city wall to the north. They were even now rolling up wine barrels and tying them together with ropes. Like ants on an ant hill they were hurrying and scurrying, carrying, loading and unloading.

The Emperor and Giustiniani with grim determination decided upon their course of action. Nicholas, the Emperor's guard, was sent to call a meeting of the twelve key men of the defense, and within an hour they were assembled in the palace. The meeting was carried on quietly, swiftly, surreptitiously, with no pomp and circumstance.

Four nights later—as a result of this conference—

the defenders made their counterattack. The plan, suggested by James Coco, a captain from the Black Sea, was to make a dash and burn the enemy ships. The necessary number of men volunteered, and Coco himself offered to lead the assault.

Two hours before dawn two imperial ships, accompanied by two Venetian galleys, well armed and carrying men and materials for burning the Turkish fleet, moved soundlessly out from the Greek docks. But just as they did so, a flare went up from the Galata tower. The sailors stopped dead, oars suspended. Coco, impatient to get on, refused to take the flare as a warning. Pushing out ahead of the others, he moved on toward the Turkish ships lying ominously quiet in the dark harbor.

All of a sudden, with a roar of cannon, the Turkish ships came to life.

Coco's ship, out in front, was immediately destroyed, and Coco himself perished. The largest of the galleys was then attacked and had to be abandoned.

Certain Genoese of Galata had obviously betrayed the plans to Mohammed. The mocking laughter of the Turks aboard ship rang through the night.

Two ships of the defenders were now left, on which eighty Turkish ships in the harbor let loose their guns. But the two had guns and men of their own, and though so mightily outnumbered they were not captured. The fighting lasted until dawn, when with their men still safe they returned to their moorings.

The sailors from the abandoned galley, however, did not return. They had been seen by the men of the other ships, swimming for shore. But when the count was taken, forty were missing.

The Emperor had not gone to bed all night. Down on his knees before the ikon he prayed to the Virgin for the lives of those forty men. He was still on his knees when he heard a shrill terrified scream.

A Greek serving woman had brought breakfast to her master who had been patrolling the wall below the palace. It was her scream that the Emperor had heard. Others heard it too—frightened wives and mothers whose menfolk had gone out that night and not come back. Now they rushed to the ramparts and stared in horror across the harbor.

On the opposite shore, each on a high pole by itself, hung forty lifeless heads. The Greeks crowding upon the walls moaned. The Emperor seated on his horse gazed across with sorrowing eyes.

While he paused there, momentarily alone, infinitely saddened, the clank of heavy armor brought him back to the world of decisions and action.

Gabriel Trevisano, the Venetian captain in charge of the Greek ships, stood before him. He was a short man, heavy and rugged. Salt and spray, or perhaps premature age, had dappled his brown beard with white. His rough seaman's face was red and angry.

"We'll have 200 heads!" he barked savagely, with only a brusque nod to acknowledge that he stood before the Greek monarch.

He was not asking permission, he was stating a plan of action. Two hundred Turks had been captured a few days earlier in the naval battle at the mouth of the harbor and were still alive, held as prisoners. By noon that day, in retaliation, 200 Turkish heads hung high on pikes on the Greek ramparts facing the shore of Galata.

"But it can never bring back our own," mourned the Emperor, "the pride of their fathers and the strength of the city!"

The Emperor's heart was heavy. The people of the city had reached their point of lowest depression.

17

THE DEFENDERS STAND FAST

The new Turkish bridge was now built, 1000 wine barrels bound together and covered with a solid floor. Across this floating battery the Turks began to wheel big guns. The eighty ships that had come overland were unloading scaling ladders. Besides six miles of landward walls, strong indeed, but fiercely pounded with all the force the enemy could muster, the Greeks now must defend their weakest wall.

The city had never before in its history been in such danger. Its defenders were ready to die, but they wanted to save their Emperor. He must leave the city before it was too late.

A ship lay ready, prepared to take him aboard and set sail at an hour's notice. If he waited longer, escape might be impossible.

When his loyal supporters came to the palace and stated their proposition, he shook his head. He was too touched to speak.

Even Giustiniani urged him to go. He might be able to get help from outside, the big Genoese argued. He could go to the Morea (southern Greece) and plead the plight of the city!

As his companion-in-defense spoke, the Emperor's eyes filled with tears.

"Sire!" cried Giustiniani, emotion for the first time flushing his hard weather-beaten face. "It is for the good of Constantinople!"

But the Emperor could not be persuaded. "Ask me instead to remain with you! I am ready to die for you!" He was their Good Shepherd, he tried to tell them, who laid down his life for his sheep.

The greatest military siege of history up to that time was now approaching its fierce and terrible climax.

On May 7th the Sultan attempted a second assault. All day the people of Constantinople felt a premonition of evil. Ships were moving. Cannon pounded with a new persistence. But it was not until four hours after sunset that the attack started. Then 30,000 Turks tried to force an entrance with scaling ladders near the Crooked Gate. But the besieged resisted, and before morning the enemy withdrew.

On May 12th Mohammed threw in 50,000 men, this time at the Gate of Adrianople. The shouts of the oncoming invaders were terrifying, and the people within the walls thought that the end had come. But again the defenders pushed them back with frightful losses to the enemy.

Bravery became savagery. Decent men became fiends. Even though every Greek or Italian head that showed above the battlements was shot, there was still some hand-to-hand fighting. A Turk named Amer Bey, the Sultan's standard bearer, was attacked by a Greek, his followers put to flight, and Amer himself cut in two. The furious Turks, learning their leader's fate, returned to face sure death, but first put a sword through the heart of the Greek who had killed Amer.

The Turkish ships made sorties on the Christian ships in the harbor; they tried to destroy the Boom, but the Turks hadn't a chance against the sea-devil Venetians.

Every kind of weapon was brought into action against the walls. Ancient methods of warfare mingled with what at that day was modern. Cannon were used along with mechanical engines for casting stones. Modern gunfire was used with liquid fire. Bullets picked off a head here, a horse there, while the old-time battering ram was still being launched.

But no one in the beleaguered city was prepared for the weapon that the Turks now brought into action.

This was a tower as high as any of the four towers of the Gate of St. Romanos—a tower that moved and that was now approaching the city with slow, terrible intentness. If a modern tank had suddenly appeared, it could not have struck greater terror into the inhabitants. Giustiniani ordered the citizens away from the walls, but horror and curiosity held them. They stood spellbound, staring in terror until the monster got so close they could see the fire in its eyes.

It was a siege tower three stories high, coming over the hard beaten earth on rollers. On each floor were loopholes—its eyes—for guns and arrows. When it came to a stop, men ran out of the lower floor, their bodies covered with branches and timbers, which they flung into the ditch; out and in, and out again. A ladder was thrown out from the top floor to the wall—an improvised bridge across which ran soldiers in red fezzes. Out of every loophole came a fierce peppering of gunshot.

In the background, in his enormous white turban, the Sultan Mohammed could be seen on his horse, cheering his men on, exultant.

This must be the end. The old men and the women

in the city ran back to their houses and cowered, calling the children to them.

All day long the great mechanical beast beat down its three-way terror—rammed and bombarded and shelled. The Emperor and Giustiniani, standing shoulder to shoulder, saw one of the towers of St. Romanos begin to sway. They could do nothing. The ancient tower trembled and shook; and just as darkness came, it fell crumbling to the ground.

This indeed must be the end.

But within a half hour the defenders went to work. Every man who could leave the other walls was summoned, and together, throughout the hours of the night, they performed a superhuman feat. They cleared the ditch, rebuilt the tower at least to a standing position, and then, with supreme daring, they set fire to the Turks' wooden turret and completely demolished it.

A night's work indeed!

Mohammed was as furiously angry the next morning as he had been deliriously happy the evening before. The pashas and the viziers trembled before his wrath.

He had one more weapon—held until now in reserve. If sheer size could annihilate, then the new cannon devised by Urbann, the Hungarian, should have ended the siege of Constantinople. This was the cannon for which a new foundry had been built in Adrianople. It had taken three months to cast it and two months to bring it down the 150 miles to Constantinople. It weighed 30,000 pounds. Thirty wagons linked together were required to carry it and a hundred oxen to pull them. Two hundred and fifty workmen marched ahead to level off the rough road and repair any bridge that might be down, for this was not the day of highways. Two hundred more men walked on either side to support the unwieldy structure in case it rolled or listed.

This tremendous artillery piece fired a ball that weighed 600 pounds and traveled a mile. The explosion could be felt more than twelve miles in all directions.

If the siege tower was a mechanical dinosaur, this was the ancient equivalent of an atom bomb.

Yet it did not win the battle.

As a piece of artillery the Urbann cannon was not so successful nor so deadly as the hopeful Turks and the horrified Greeks expected. It was too big. It took two hours to load; it required the services of 500 artillerymen and in all was such an operation that it could be discharged only seven times a day. Actually the fourth time it was discharged it is said to have burst. A Turkish historian said that the explosion "tore its inventor to pieces." But one wonders. Could it be that the Sultan in his mad fury had a hand in the inventor's destruction?

Mohammed was like a wild man. He cursed the prophets who had misled him with hopes of victory.

He lashed out against soldiers and officers as well as at the scientists who had made a fool of him with their siege tower and their miracle-making cannon.

Yet Turkish cannon still lined the whole stretch of wall on the land side, and more guns continued to come over the bridge from Galata on the water side. On all sides the deafening roar of cannon continued. A man couldn't think. A woman had to scream in her nervous fear.

The Turks were learning from experience. The big cannon had burst because of overheated metal, so now after each explosion they poured oil into the mouth of the other cannon. When they found that straight-away shots, however steady, could not breach the wall, they worked out the principle of aiming at two opposite sides of a tower.

How long could the little garrison within the walls hold out?

To pay his mercenaries—the Venetian and Genoese professional soldiers and the handful of other Westerners who were loyal because they were paid to be loyal, and fought because it was their business to fight —Constantine had to dip into the church treasure. The Greeks who had rebelled against union with the Latin church now cried, "Blasphemy!" They refused to acknowledge that the treasure was paid out to save this same church from the infidel.

The Great Duke Notaros, at heart with these people

On each floor of the siege tower were loopholes for guns.

and always ready for politic-religious reasons to take sides against the Emperor, began to quarrel with Giustiniani.

When Giustiniani asked Notaros for extra cannon to defend the Gate of St. Romanos, Notaros haughtily refused.

"Traitor!" cried Giustiniani. "Why should I not cut you down!"

"Because you're a coward!"

Everyone's nerves were on edge. In the streets the Venetians and Genoese were fighting among themselves. The Emperor himself had to go into the city to intervene. Was war not bad enough, he asked them, that they must try to kill each other? He implored them to make up their quarrels and once more be friends. Gradually, under his restraining influence, both sides quieted down and order was restored.

In the meantime the battle raged. Women were called on to help repair the wall at night and with them the older children and the old men and the priests. Tombstones were taken out of the cemetery and piled up to help fill the holes in the wall. The cries of the wounded filled the city with despair.

Again a breach was made in the Outer Wall. Again the Turks tried to fill the ditch, hurling barrels and branches and tree trunks, and before they were through, driving their own men to slaughter. With pashas snapping their long switches behind them, the

Turks rushed headlong into the ditch, and fell there, man upon man, buried in the debris.

The city had been besieged for six weeks. Day and night the guns had pounded.

The little brigantine that had set sail so gallantly in April to search the promised Western ships had returned unrewarded. There were no ships. The journey had been in vain. But the brave men who had volunteered to go had now, of their own free will, come back to fight. "Whether the city be taken or not, whether it is to life or death—it is our duty to return!"

The full force of the Turkish cannon was now concentrated on the Gate of St. Romanos over the River Lycus.

On May 23rd all four of the gate towers crumbled and were leveled to the earth.

18

THE OPPOSING LEADERS

On May 24th the guns were strangely silent.

Mohammed sat cross-legged on a cushion, a shining scimitar on the ground beside him, his prayer rug in front. For the first time the Sultan felt reasonably sure of victory. But victory was going to be costly. The curtains of his silken tent were drawn aside and out beyond his armed guard he could see the white caps of his Janizaries. To enter the city of Constantinople he would have to sacrifice a fourth of those brave men. Maybe a half. He looked them over with calculation, not with pity.

The image of the blue-eyed, curly-bearded Constantine came between him and the troops. The Christian knew that he could never win. But he would fight.

Or would he?

Mohammed's black brows met in a frown. With a warrior's cynical contempt for all men of peace, he decided on a new approach. Standing up abruptly he sent for two of his pashas.

About an hour later two turbaned men in rich robes, mounted on Arabian steeds, could be seen riding across the Turkish camp toward the Gate of St. Romanos. Before them rode heralds carrying long trumpets, and beside them ran messengers in uniforms of green.

The Emperor and Giustiniani were together on the harbor side of the walls when Nicholas, the palace guard, approached and stood deferentially behind them.

Constantine nodded to him to speak.

The Sultan had sent an ambassador, the guard said, and his train was even now approaching the palace gate. A gleam of excitement—perhaps of hope— lighted the usually impassive face.

The two men looked straight at each other:

Giustiniani, ruddy, healthy, strongly masculine; the Emperor, almost spiritual in his worn, tired beauty. They needed no words for understanding.

Constantine turned his horse's head and rode swiftly toward the Blachernae. Still in armor and aching with the weariness of the past night, he arrived in time to receive the Turkish emissary.

To his dismay he saw that it was two emissaries, and that neither was his friend, Khalil Pasha.

The first Vizier spoke. *His master, the Great Sultan, presented his greetings to the Emperor. It was imperative, the Great Sultan said, that the two rulers come to an understanding. An end to fighting was desirable and time was short.* The emissary's glance slanted down toward the four enormous piles of rubble that once were noble towers. *Herein,* he pronounced, holding out a roll of parchment, *were the Sultan's terms of surrender.*

They were not bad terms. If the Emperor would leave the city, Mohammed would lift the siege. He would grant the Emperor the land of Morea, and Emperor and Sultan could thus live in peace, he said. To all the people he offered safety, and for those who wished to leave, a safe departure from the city.

But the insurmountable barrier remained. Though it was not uttered in so many words, Mohammed II would be master of Constantinople. The 1000-year-old stronghold of the Christian world would be in the hands of the infidel Turk. Constantinople would be Moslem.

From the first sight of the richly clad, elegant ambassadors, the Emperor Constantine knew what his answer must be. No matter how tempting the offer, no matter if it meant security for himself for the rest of his life and food and comfort once more for his harassed people, he could never hand over his city to the Turks.

Between diplomats, however, there must be ceremony. Constantine heard the Sultan's ambassador through in silence. He bowed his head ever so slightly in monarchical graciousness when the two men departed.

The Emperor then summoned the Greek nobles, the high-ranking Venetians, and the Genoese, that he himself should not alone be responsible for the sure slaughter that lay ahead. Both Greeks and Latins agreed that the Sultan's peace offer must be refused. It was to be a fight to the finish. They also agreed with the Emperor that Phranza should be their ambassador to give the Sultan his answer.

When they had left him alone, Constantine, as was his custom, knelt down before the ikon. He saw no faint ray of hope. But it was in the nobility of his nature to prefer a martyr's death to a city's humiliation.

Mohammed stamped his foot in maniacal fury when

the Emperor's answer was delivered to him. The capture of Constantinople meant more to him at that moment than the lives of all his people.

Khalil Pasha, as number one Grand Vizier, still tried with suave argument to dissuade him. But the other pashas were firmly behind their Sultan.

"Whoever shall capture the city shall have his sins forgiven," the Prophet had said. "Happy the prince, happy the army, that shall achieve its conquest!"

With Allah behind him Mohammed now proclaimed the day of annihilation. On May 29th: an assault on all sides of the city at the same time!

At once the huge encampment sprang into feverish activity. The military preparations of months and the religious teachings of a lifetime were about to culminate in desperate battle.

On the evening of the 27th, the Sultan issued his final orders. Twelve heralds on horseback, reins in one hand, a long trumpet of brass held high in the other, rode among the troops announcing the day.

In Moslem fashion, the soldiers purified their bodies with water, then purified their minds with prayer. They began their fast, for no food or drink would enter their bodies until night of the next day.

Then when the sun went down, the dervishes came forth. Among the tents of the soldiers they danced and twirled in their long black skirts and pointed hats, circling slowly, then faster and faster, around each other and around each tent, their wide skirts straight out from their bodies. Theirs were the ecstatic promises of eternity! Those who died fighting for Allah would be wafted by hovering angels to the rivers and gardens of paradise. There they would spend an immortal youth in the arms of beautiful black-eyed maidens.

The men were frenzied to the point of madness. To die or to live—it was one to them. "Allah is Allah; there is no god but Allah and Mahomet is his prophet."

To the alluring promises of the dervishes, the Sultan added more material rewards. For those who captured the city, he promised all its riches. "The city and the buildings are mine," proclaimed Mohammed, "but the captives and the spoil, the treasures of gold and jewels, will be yours."

To the specific soldier who first scaled the wall, he would grant his wealthiest province. "Many are the fair provinces of my empire," he said in ringing voice. "The brave soldier who first ascends the walls of Constantinople shall be made governor of the fairest and wealthiest of these provinces."

But a deserter—he added in tones of thunder—had he even the wings of a bird, could never go fast enough to escape the Sultan's vengeance.

The campfires blazed from Galata to the farthest

point of the sea, a half moon of flame—the symbol of destruction.

Within the city of Constantinople Mohammed's plans were known almost as soon as in his own camp. Before dawn on the morning of May 28th, the Emperor was on his horse going the rounds of the towers, speaking to the sentinels, encouraging them. In this time of peril his good friend Phranza rode by his side. They had nearly completed the circuit when the first rays of rosy dawn tinted the eastern sky. At the Crooked Gate, close to the palace, they dismounted.

The guards in the tower told them that all night they had heard subdued sounds outside the walls—the soft thud of big movements. In silence the Turks had been dragging up their machines of war. They were now just beyond the moat. But not a man's voice had the guards heard. Not a shout. Not an order. It was a mighty pantomime played in the dark.

Up on the tower, protected from view, the Emperor and Phranza could just make out the vast military panorama that stretched up and over the hill as far as eye could reach, troops and cannon still advancing like great unearthly shadows.

Back in the Blachernae the Emperor put on his robe of purple and for the last time summoned to him the noblest of the Greeks and the bravest of their Latin allies. With Phranza at his right hand, he addressed these men who had stood beside him so long and so faithfully.

He spoke of the city, refuge of all Christians, the pride and joy of every Greek who lived in Eastern lands, the Queen of Cities, that in earlier times had subdued all the nations of the earth. The enemy coveted it because it was the greatest prize. But the enemy were wild men without intelligence. With noise and shouts they tried to frighten and intimidate. "We are few in numbers beside them," he said sadly. "But we are skillful in warfare; in bravery and strength of will and nobility, we are a match for them!"

He turned to the Genoese and Venetians and addressed them separately, thanking them deeply for the valiant service they had given.

In grave silence all present listened to his words. Constantine had no hope of victory within himself, yet he infused into their souls something of the ardor and courage with which he himself was inspired. It grew out of loyalty and pride and devotion. He had no Mohammedan promises of heaven to offer and no compensation except honor. They had fought together long and well. They had resisted onslaught after onslaught of an implacable foe. They were still here. They were still unbeaten!

When he had finished they all embraced—rough generals, elegant aristocrats, the Emperor. Tears sprang to the eyes of the hardest men there. "We will die for the faith of Christ and for our country!"

In the afternoon a solemn procession marched slowly through the city to Sancta Sophia. It was led by the heads of the two churches, the Orthodox Patriarch and the Roman Cardinal. This was a tribute to the Emperor who had begged them to face the crisis together. Priests and monks, nobles and soldiers followed. All rivalries were cast aside on this day of days; and in the spirit of perfect and harmonious unity, the people of Constantinople entered the most beautiful church in Christendom together for the last time. It was the final scene in a millennium of gorgeous Byzantine pageantry.

The great church was filled. Hundreds of lamps enfolded the whole interior in a glow of soft light. Aloft in the golden dome, the huge figure of Christ leaned over them, gazing down upon His people for perhaps the last time. There were priests and monks, women carrying candles, soldiers in armor who had left the walls for an hour's respite and had come to pray. All were there to implore God to save their city.

From every part of the church rose voices in solemn chant. The creed was recited, first in Greek and then in Latin. All who could reach the high altar, went forward with folded hands to receive the body of Christ.

When Mass was over, none wanted to leave the sacred walls and the packed companionship of his fellow creatures. For the first time in many months all the people of Constantinople were united in a single cause.

The Emperor embraced those who stood near him, workmen and nobles, Greeks and Latins, priests and soldiers. Then alone he walked out of the church and in his purple robes mounted his horse.

Each commander went to his assigned station. Every gate and each portion of wall had its own defender. The Great Duke Notaros, as high admiral of the fleet, was given command of those portions of the wall that lay along the harbor side. One of the few remaining foes of East and West unity, of Giustiniani, even of the Emperor, there he was, on guard where the walls were least defensible—where the prows of Turkish ships were so close that they almost touched the houses of the city.

All evening the alarm bells rang through the city calling men, women and children to their posts. Those who could not fight carried stones to the walls to be thrown down on the enemy. Some of the women brought mantles to protect their men; others, ikons to comfort them with the thought of their Saviour.

Shortly after midnight the Emperor and Phranza went to all the stations on a last roundup of inspection.

Then, in the dark of the Hippodrome, the Emperor reviewed his troops. The little army was to take its stand in the space between the Outer and Inner Walls.

The gates of the Inner Wall were to be closed and locked that none could re-enter the city. Giustiniani had put it up to the men, but it was the soldiers themselves who arrived at the decision voluntarily. They were there to conquer or to die.

This was the final review.

19

THE FALL

Long before daybreak of May 29th, at a precise moment between one and two o'clock in the morning, a hideous din rose from the entire periphery of the city. From the throat of every Turk in the surrounding plain came a fearful yell.

Dervishes and soldiers set the tents afire at a given signal, making a circle of flame from the Sea of Marmora to the Golden Horn. "Tomorrow," they cried, "we sleep in Constantinople!"

Mohammed charged his troops. He swore an oath by the eternity of God, by the 4000 prophets, by the soul of his father Murad, by the lives of his children and by his scimitar.

With pounding drums and shrill pipes and the mad cries of thousands, the attack started. Screaming men leaped forward the entire length of the land wall. When they reached the edge of the moat, they could not stop because of the masses behind them. They were forced into the moat; and as they fell in, others leaped over their bodies or fell beside them.

It was not just a wild sortie. Every move had been plotted with strict military precision. The city was surrounded along its whole circumference during the night. The ditch had been partially filled. The Turkish ships were close to the walls, ready to supply men and guns and scaling ladders on the water side.

The first wave of attackers were the volunteers—untrained herdsmen and nomads armed only with swords and spears. They had come for the promise of loot and reward. There was little order among them and there were no commanders; but should a single man try to turn back, a vizier or pasha was behind him with iron mace or loaded whip. It was the job of this unwieldy mob to throw up scaling ladders, and the Turks from behind shot a curtain of arrows to give them protection.

But it was not enough. The Greeks on the walls poured liquid fire and boiling pitch down over them, and the men ascending fell screaming below. The ditch was already covered with the bodies of men writhing in agony. To the Sultan these were more useful dead than living. They were a bridge over which ran the second mass of attackers.

The second assault was made by Christian mercenaries—adventurers and ne'er-do-wells, in the Sultan's army as professionals. These troops were organized and trained. They advanced the length of the line in companies of a thousand men each. Behind them, too, were the pashas and viziers; and should any escape their vigilance, the Janizaries coming up in the rear were ready with scimitars to cut them down. When the mercenaries reached the scaling ladders, they in turn were stoned and burned and flung to the earth below.

The defenders fought with merciless ferocity. For forty days they had had no rest, but desperation gave them strength. The Emperor on the ramparts near the Gate of St. Romanos and Giustiniani, fighting with his men between the walls near that same gate, were a constant inspiration to the men. Theirs was the most dangerous sector, and it was here that the Sultan was directing the heaviest attack.

The third troops to fling themselves upon the walls were the Turks trained in Asia—small men in red caps and scimitars, savage fighters who needed no spurring. They were fighting for Islam. "Allah! Allah! There is no god but Allah!" they cried as they leaped forward to meet the enemy. None from this division tried to escape. Still they could not climb the stockade.

The handful of Greeks continued to have the advantage. They fired on the hundreds and thousands that came in each new wave. They poured their boiling pitch and squirted liquid fire. They used their little ammunition with precision.

But the Turkish drums continued to roll, and the trumpets sounded. From the boats and the bridge and the land side, the artillery thundered. Smoke rose in thick clouds on all sides of the city.

For two hours the defense held. The Turks could get not an inch of foothold on the wall. But the break in the wall at the Gate of St. Romanos was now 1000 feet wide. Inside, Giustiniani with 2000 men waited for the onslaught, the breastplates of the Genoese cuirassiers glittering menacingly in the light of gunshot and flung torches.

It was a decisive moment, and the Sultan met it with his greatest strength. Riding abreast them, mace in hand, his large white turban visible even in the darkness, Mohammed advanced with his choicest troops, those that he had saved for the final thrust—the Janizaries. Fresh, vigorous, the best-trained fighters in the world, they poured through the breach and across the half-filled ditch, their white hats rising like the breakers of the sea as they mounted closer and closer. It was a sight to strike terror into the most stalwart defense. . . .

It may be that these troops of fearful renown turned the tide of battle.

But more likely it was the loss of Giustiniani. The Greeks were still holding off the Janizaries in spite of the missiles hurled on them from behind the lines, when the great captain was wounded by an arrow. Bent over in pain he made his way toward the Emperor on the rampart.

"I'm finished!" he cried out bitterly through the din of battle.

The Emperor refused to believe him. "Your wound is but slight!" he called back. To lose Giustiniani was to lose his two arms and his heart.

But Giustiniani shook his head. "Sire, I leave you." His voice was strangled but insistent. "I must have the key. I must get inside."

He who had called for the vow of sacrifice was the first to break it. He was through. He would command no longer.

The Emperor, deeply unwilling, unlocked the gate; and the big man went through it. Soldiers near by paused in their fighting as their leader disappeared.

Their faces dripped with sweat. The blood of wounds slowly reddened the stones on which they stood. They had been fighting desperately for three hours.

Because he was a Genoese, and because the Genoese had made for themselves a reputation of disloyalty and unreliability, some historians have condemned Giustiniani. But others have defended him saying he knew the seriousness of his wound.

Giustiniani was back once more in the circumscribed city where he had lived so intensely and to such purpose for the past four months. He plodded through its narrow alleyways to the Boom, off which his ship was anchored. Headed west, toward the home he would never see, he died on the ship six days later.

But his commander never knew. To Constantine it was the desertion of his closest companion and co-fighter. The last the Emperor saw was the broad back as Giustiniani left him, head down, and walked out into an almost empty city street.

Many of Giustiniani's Genoese soldiers followed him. The opening of that gate was a terrible temptation. The ease of it—the escape from sure death—was more than many could bear.

The defection of the Western fighters shattered the defense—particularly at the Gate of St. Romanos. The Turks now outnumbered the Christians a hundred to one. Their cannon never ceased pounding. The Janizaries came in wave upon wave. The attack pressed mercilessly on until at last the great walls, that had withstood the shocks of a thousand years, slowly crumbled into a heap of ruins.

Yet every Christian still alive was ready with brandished sword to pierce the heart of the oncoming enemy. The fight was not over.

At this crisis a wild cry came from within the city. *"Aleo e polis!* The city is lost!" The brave men fighting at St. Romanos stopped as if turned to stone. Through the demolished wall they could see the Gate of Kerkoporta, and high on its tower the red flag of the Turks unfurled to the breeze.

"The city is lost!" The cry tore its way through the charged air of the beleaguered city.

The Emperor galloped over to the Kerkoporta only to find that the news was false. A few Turks had entered, but already they had been vanquished by the defenders. It was a suicide squad sent in to tear down the Greek flag and the Venetian banner of St. Mark and to hoist the red Turkish standard in their place. How they got in no one in the confusion seemed to know; but by the time the Emperor reached the gate, the brief bloody contest was over, and in a matter of minutes the red flag was down.

But ironically, the garrison that had fought so long and so heroically on the walls suddenly collapsed. Panic seized them with the first sight of the foreign flag. Soldiers threw down their arms and rushed off the walls, heroism drained out of them. They ran with the populace through the streets.

Not all ran. The Emperor, back with his men, hastily got off his horse and took up a shield. He was now in command. The Greeks fought in a circle close around him. Phranza was still there, even though too old to fight.

Mohammed, aware of the disorder, pushed harder. His white horse could be seen behind the troops—his big turban, his shining scimitar.

The walls, a mass of enormous loose blocks almost undefended, were scaled at last.

It was a giant Janizary who made the first entrance over the wall into the city. Hassan was of enormous stature and strength. With round shield held close against his body, he scaled the wall. Thirty of his fellow Janizaries came after him, but eighteen were instantly slain. Hassan reached the top of the wall, stood there for all to see, and was then flung down by the defenders. Wounded, he fought on his knees, pulled himself up, then fell again under the darts and stones that continued to pound down upon him. But he was the first. He it was who should have been awarded the Sultan's fairest province. But Hassan did not live to enjoy his triumph.

He had, however, proved that it could be done. Mohammed had made his point. Now hundreds of Turks swarmed over the fallen walls and towers where Hassan had shown the way. They came in such numbers that the Greeks could no longer hold them off. The defenders were trapped in the enclosure between the walls. In that small confined space, men were falling upon one another, swords striking out wildly, shields and armor clanking.

In the midst of the melee was Constantine. Most of the men around him were either slain by the onrush of the enemy or violently pushed away. The last words that Phranza heard were: "Can a Christian be found to kill me?" With this the Emperor rushed, sword outheld, into a knot of five Janizaries. It has been said that of the five he killed three and that the others slashed his face and dug a sword in his back. But no one can ever know. Constantine disappeared from Phranza's view, and his body was buried under a mountain of the dead.

After the Emperor's death, resistance and order vanished. The victorious Turkish soldiers rushed through the breaches of the wall at St. Romanos and were joined by others who had made an entrance on the harbor side.

Just after the sun rose, Mohammed saw that his objective had been won.

After a siege of fifty-three days, Constantinople— venerable stronghold that had defied the Persian, the

Roman, the Avar, the Bulgar, the Caliphs—was irretrievably defeated by the army of Mohammed II.

At noon of that day, May 29, 1453, Sultan Mohammed II, known from that time on as Mohammed the Conqueror, made his triumphal entry through the Gate of Adrianople. He proceeded slowly on his prancing white horse, through the city to Sancta Sophia. The cymbals crashed and the gongs resounded. The drums beat without cease.

20

THE CONQUEROR, THE TRAITOR
AND THE MARTYR

On the walls of Constantinople the last Roman Emperor
met his fate. Close by the Gate of St. Romanos, Constantine Paleologus, successor of Constantine the
Great, died a hero's death.

After the battle was over, a pair of crimson shoes
embroidered with golden imperial eagles was dug
out from under the heap of slain. No one could have

said which body was the Emperor's, but on the Sultan's order the Janizaries brought him a corpse so badly mutilated that the Emperor's closest friend could not have recognized it. The head was severed from the body, stuffed with straw and hung up on the statue of Justinian for all the population to see.

The Gate of St. Romanos was blocked forever. Unlike all the other gates and walls, its crumpled ruins and the ruins of the walls north of it were not repaired. Did Mohammed leave them standing as a monument of victory? Or was it that posterity should not be reminded, in passing over those hallowed stones, of the brave men who had sacrificed all for the honor of their city?

The Sultan did not enter the city with his troops. The Janizaries scaled the walls and after heavy losses got through; a somewhat larger troop of Turks, coming from the harbor side, met them; and behind both wedges the whole army, scimitars aloft, poured into the city, shouting. But Mohammed remained aloof, true to the promise he had made his soldiers. "To those who capture the city, to them are its riches and its people!"

And what of the people?

When the red flag of the Turks was seen above the wicket gate of Kerkoporta—a false signal as it turned out to be—all the people who could, scurried to Sancta Sophia, men, women, mothers holding babies in their arms, children clinging to their skirts. The earlier rush of courage had drained away. Cowed and terrified, they were now packed solidly into the church. They barred the doors. While their Emperor was fighting and dying for them in the first morning rays of that day of horror, they huddled together in the dark sanctuary.

They were praying. They were listening—still unaware that their city had fallen—for the whir of angels' wings. They looked for that angel who, as the monks had promised, was to meet the oncoming enemy and halt him.

When they heard pounding at the doors of the church, some of them were still hopeful. But it was no angel come to deliver them. It was the enemy breaking through the doors with axes.

Once in, the Turks rushed headlong into the stupefied mob. Their shouts in a strange tongue resounded over the low moaning of the people.

The Turks picked and chose among their prisoners. Forcing the Greeks to file out of the church in some kind of order, they separated the obviously rich from the miserably poor, for that way lay treasure. They bound the males with cords, and the females—after separating the young and beautiful from the old and haggard—they bound with their own veils. All ranks were tied together indiscriminately, prelates of the church with workmen, senators with slaves. In long lines the conquerors thus drove the Greeks out of the church and through the streets of their own city.

Of the inhabitants of the city who had not been caught in the church, many tried to escape by ship. They ran through the streets, down the steep hills to the harbor where Genoese and Venetian ships were preparing to get away. The beach was covered with terrified people. Many jumped into the water and swam from ship to ship. But the seamen refused to take them aboard, always giving preference to their own countrymen. Even the Genoese of Galata were fleeing the country in great numbers, though the Sultan had made them many promises.

The greatest city in the world, grown big and rich and old, was now entirely in the hands of the Ottoman Turks. The march from the plains of Asia that had taken 250 years had reached its end. Fighting Islamites, Christian mercenaries in the pay of Islam, camp followers and ignorant herdsmen from Anatolia, now thrust their hands deep into what was left of the wealth of Constantinople. On the surface the city was poor, but it had a wealth of subterranean riches. Many of the nobles had hidden their rich garments of satin and furs, their jewels, their silver. They had buried gold ingots and old coin, safe from the needs and demands of their Emperor. Some of them now disclosed the hiding places in the hope of buying safety from the marauders. In the monasteries and the churches, the looters still found treasure in abundance —pearls, vases of gold and silver, ecclesiastical chalices, incense burners, sacred ornaments.

It was a repetition of what the Latins of the Fourth Crusade had done. Out of the Byzantine libraries, 120,000 manuscripts disappeared. To the Turks these were hardly worth the effort. For ten volumes they could get only a single ducat—even though there might be an Aristotle or Homer among them. Fortunately, because the Genoese and the Venetians were ready to trade under gunfire if a bargain showed, many of these books of incalculable value turned up eventually in Italy. With the classical knowledge they spread, these stolen books ironically became one of the foundation stones of the Renaissance.

For seven hours thousands of Turks were on the rampage. No woman was safe. No work of art was too precious for their rough hands. Loot and people— these were their promised reward.

At noon Mohammed II, the Conqueror, rode into the city in triumph. All the fighting, all the looting, all the tragedy, the devastation, begun before daylight on that fatal day of May 29th, had already become history. Mohammed came on his slowly prancing white charger through the Gate of Adrianople, which from that day on became the gate of victors. Sultans returning from their conquests in the centuries to come,

168

always entered Constantinople through the Gate of Adrianople.

With the Conqueror were his special guard of viziers, pashas, tsauches, picked for their build, their height and their strength—"robust as Hercules, dexterous as Apollo, and equal in battle to any ten of the race of ordinary mortals."

Most of them were seeing Constantinople from within its walls for the first time. Sitting their horses with the ease of men born to the saddle, they turned their turbaned heads but slightly from side to side, not to seem overeager. But their black eyes shone as they stared at the lordly domes and pillars and palaces of the fabled city.

At the world-renowned Hippodrome, the Sultan stopped. It was a shambles now and had been since the Latins destroyed it in 1204. But in the center of what was left there was still the ancient column of the twisted serpents. High spirits must have shot extra strength into his arm; for now, from his horse's back, Mohammed with his iron mace shattered the under jaw of one of the huge stone creatures.

At Sancta Sophia he dismounted. The Greek crowds had by now been largely disposed of and led away. Only his own men were in the church. As the Sultan entered, a Turk was hacking away at a marble slab of the pavement with his ax.

169

"The loot and the people are yours," roared Mohammed. "But the city and the buildings are mine!"

Pashas, viziers and guards entered behind their ruler.

Sancta Sophia had already become a Mohammedan Mosque. On the very day that Mohammed rode triumphantly into the city, the muezzin ascended the loftiest turret of the noblest church in Christendom, and from its height chanted in loud clear tones his call to the men of Islam to come and pray in the name of Allah.

After visiting Sancta Sophia, the Sultan went to the palace of Blachernae. He smiled cynically as he viewed the empty rooms. "The spider has woven his web in the imperial palace, and the owl hath sung her watch song on the towers of Afrasiab."

Mohammed was a learned man who could thus quote from Persian verse. But the blood of the Asian primitive still pulsed in his veins.

He now called the Great Duke Notaros to him. When it was officially established that the Emperor had fallen and was dead, the Great Duke became the first man in the realm.

Notaros came into the presence of the conqueror bearing gifts out of his own treasure. He had not hidden it in vain; and behind him now came his servants carrying silver plate, a jeweled tiara, magnificent goblets.

The Duke bowed low in front of the new monarch who sat cross-legged on a cushion in the otherwise almost empty Blachernae Palace. Mohammed's turbaned head was held proudly high.

"They are yours, Sire," the Duke said, pointing to the gifts in his servants' arms. "And here am I, your faithful servant."

Mohammed who only that morning had ordered the bloody head of Constantine hung high, stared now at the sleek, bearded nobleman bowing before him. Being learned in many languages, he addressed Notaros in Greek. "Why did you not employ these treasures in the defense of your ruler and your country?"

"God has reserved them for you, Sire," said Notaros humbly.

"If God reserved them for me," said the Sultan, "how is it that you have allowed such a long and bitter battle to come between them and me?"

The Great Duke said that he had feared to trust an emissary. He had already been witness to the treachery of one of his majesty's most honored viziers.

Khalil Pasha, behind the Sultan, remained stonily aloof.

The interview ended on a bad note. When the Great Duke left the Sultan's presence, he did so with little confidence. Nothing had been accomplished, except that his servants, returning with him, were now empty-handed.

171

But following the interview there came what seemed to be an amnesty. The Sultan moved graciously about the city. His white horse danced. The jewels on his kaftan, his outside garment, sparkled. His turban was gleaming in its whiteness under the June sun. He consoled the wives of the men who had become his prisoners. He asked his pashas and viziers to get him a list of the Greek nobles.

"Most of them died around the body of their Emperor!" Khalil Pasha told him, speaking out of a great silence.

"I speak of the rich Greeks that still live," the Sultan answered him coolly.

Eagerly these opulent citizens told the pashas and viziers their names and those of all their family. They were nine families. Each vied with the others in offering gifts, no doubt keeping aside a nice cache for himself. In a later period such men would be called "collaborators."

The Sultan was preparing a drama of his own. He was a young man brought up, in spite of his rank, in the savage life of the plains. He was likewise a young man of education, which in this case proved a dangerous combination. His cruelties could be more terrible through his greater knowledge of how men think and act and desire. He recognized the weakness of the man who bows humbly before a new and powerful ruler.

172

Rumor had spread that the Sultan, having completed his groundwork in Constantinople, was preparing to leave for his quarters in Adrianople.

Now, presumably on the eve of departure, he called a large gathering in the Hippodrome. The nine Greeks whose names he had listed were among those called. They came, smiling, bowing, bearing gifts, with their families behind them.

Once they were lined up in front of him, the Sultan asked if they were willing to submit to his rule.

To a man they shouted their affirmative answer.

By their example, he asked, would they influence the other Greeks to submit?

Again they promised.

"But where are these Greeks?" he asked, and turned his head to gaze upon the stuffed head of the Emperor Constantine still atop the statue of Justinian.

A cold wave passed over the assemblage.

"Kneel then!" the Sultan said in a louder, more imperative voice. "With your faces to the ground!"

And when they knelt with their faces to the ground, the Sultan's executioner, one by one, chopped off their heads.

The last to be called to his presence was the Great Duke Notaros who strode in confidently with his two sons. But when he saw the circle of bloody heads that surrounded the Sultan, he recognized his fate.

Rising to his full height he tried in one gesture to

repudiate his past. "I only ask that I first see my own sons struck down—that I may know the nature of their fate!"

Shrugging his shoulders Mohammed ordered the execution of the two boys. When they lay dead before him, Notaros, on order of the Sultan, was beheaded.

Crafty and secretive as he was, always ready to go back on a treaty to fit his own needs, Mohammed knew a traitor when he saw one. He doubtless recognized the Notaros party as men of whom he could never be sure and as such he destroyed them.

Through the course of centuries several versions have been told of the sequence of events that occurred on that terrible morning when the city fell, and of the precise role played by Notaros in the tragedy.

If there was treachery, it was pinpointed at the entrance of the Turks on the harbor side into the city.

How did Turkish soldiers get through the Gate of Kerkoporta? The Gate of Kerkoporta was near the palace and not far from the harbor. It had long been out of use. In fact it had been closed up back in the days of the Crusades because of a prophecy that through it the Emperor Frederick would enter the city. During the last days of this final siege, however, it had been reopened to allow an extra sortie for the defenders—one more exit through which they could dash at night to repair the walls. It lay in the sector of which Notaros was in command.

It was at the climax of the battle, when the Greeks on the Romanos sector were withstanding the heaviest bombardment, and directly after Giustiniani had been wounded, that a detachment of fifty Turks came through the undefended Kerkoporta gate. It was a well-timed attack that suggested inside information.

Who gave it?

Who started the cry: "The city is lost!"

We shall never know.

There is also no answer to the question of how a large contingent of Turks shortly afterwards poured through the Gate of Phanar. Phanar is that district on the harbor side of the city, which was also under the special guard of the Great Duke Notaros. When the twelve Janizaries, following the giant Hassan, finally scaled the landward walls and thus forced entrance through the Emperor's defense of the city, they found coming toward them a mass of Turks who had come unmolested through the Phanar Gate.

In the confusion of battle, when hundreds of men are fighting in close combat, amidst the screams of the wounded, the terrified flight of the frightened, the horrors of bodies trampled upon, no historian can be sure. Not even the reporter on the spot can be exact. Prejudices will color reason. Nevertheless the finger points accusingly toward Notaros.

Within a shorter time than seems possible, 60,000

Greeks were transported from the city to the Turkish camp and to the ships in the harbor. Later they were exchanged or sold into slavery and eventually scattered throughout the distant provinces of the Ottoman Empire.

Among those sent into servitude was Phranza, the Emperor's friend, separated from his dearly beloved wife and children. After working for a Turkish master for fifteen months, Phranza, being a highly intelligent man, succeeded in recovering his freedom. He then made his way to Adrianople where he had learned that his wife was also in captivity. In a year's time he was able to ransom her from the Turkish family with which she had been living, but not his two children. His beautiful daughter Thamar died in the Sultan's harem, aged fourteen; and his son, only a year older, killed himself rather than do the Sultan's bidding. It is to Phranza himself, who spent the remainder of his life writing the history of these times, that we owe so many intimate personal details.

Khalil Pasha, who had served both Sultan and Emperor, was arrested and tortured in many ways until he died.

Constantinople had become a Turkish city and remains a Turkish city to this day. To the plain cloth of red that was the Ottoman flag was added the crescent and star, symbol of Byzantium.

Sancta Sophia still stands, but the golden mosaics of Justinian were whitewashed and four minarets were added.

Mohammed called to him the Orthodox monk Gennadius, who had fought hardest against the union of the Western and Eastern churches, and made him Patriarch of the Christian Orthodox Church. He presented him with a robe and staff, assured him protection and favor, and gave him a palace in the Phanar region of the city, where his successor still rules. Thus Mohammed completed the rift between East and West.

Cardinal Isidore, disguised as a soldier, was captured and sold into slavery.

In order to repopulate the city, now almost empty, Mohammed encouraged new peoples to come in. He invited the Greeks who had fled to come back and gave them quarters in the same Phanar section around the palace of their Patriarch. They could not hold office, but they became the workers, the traders and the bankers, and they lived in peace. He brought whole villages from foreign soil to settle in the city—Serbs, Bulgars, Armenians—so that Constantinople today is a city of many races, many faces and many languages.

The Ottoman administration which Mohammed organized lasted down into the nineteenth century. Constantinople became again a great city—this time the Moslem, not the Christian, capital of the Levant. It is now called Istanbul.

A modern historian looking back can see much that the people of those days, blinded by hate and fear, could not recognize. How different, says the modern historian, it might have been!

If the Latins had not destroyed Constantinople in 1204.

If the Christians had united in 1396 when Timur had routed the Turks.

If instead of a mere five ships, Genoa and Venice had sent their entire navies to help the Emperor—the city might have been saved.

If in the last days the people of Constantinople had had the will to save their city. If they had had the desperate courage of the defenders of ancient Carthage, of Jerusalem, and of London under the blitz!

The honor of the Emperor Constantine XI and a handful of his faithful followers is all that is left of our story. The last Roman Emperor in the long line of Roman Emperors from Augustus on may claim the city of Constantinople as his monument.

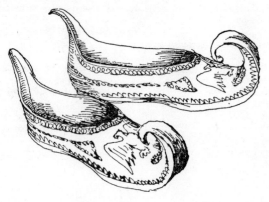

Index

179

180

5 6   A.H.   JAN '63